Molecular Genetics

A. Gib DeBusk

The Florida State University

The Macmillan Company, New York
Collier-Macmillan Limited, London

106138

First Printing

Library of Congress catalog card number: 68–11000

The Macmillan Company, New York

Collier-Macmillan Canada, Ltd., Toronto, Ontario

Printed in the United States of America

To My Wife and Colleague
  Betty
and our family
  Barrett, Brook, Clint
  Michele, Melissa, Cara

Preface

MOLECULAR GENETICS may be defined as the storage, modification, and retrieval of macromolecular information, a subject unique in that it transcends all modern biology. It has deep-rooted foundations in transmission genetics, and recombination itself is still an important genetic criterion though far from fully understood at the molecular level. The milieu of biochemical genetics in the 1950s gave rise to molecular genetics; the Watson-Crick model for DNA structure and replication was crucial in subsequent growth of the field.

It was already known that genes exerted their control over individual biochemical reactions by means of enzymes that are specialized proteins. The flow of information from DNA to RNA to protein soon became clear. Though the process occurs with surprising speed and fidelity, the system cannot be represented as a simple tape in which an unalterable pattern is followed. Instead, subtle regulatory mechanisms exist through which the cell can respond to particular components of the environment. Even mutation is not irrevocable because we now know that repair systems exist that detect and eliminate molecular mistakes in DNA.

The concept of the gene itself is profound. That biological "atom" has been split—and split again. It is no simple bead on a thread because recombination occurs freely within its boundaries—boundaries governed by the rules of punctuation of the genetic code. Genes exist that regulate other genes. Genes may be stored as DNA in a test tube for years yet be used to perpetuate their own type when supplied with the cellular machinery for replication. Genes from one organism may even take up residence alongside genes of a host organism.

We saw these and other exciting discoveries in the early life of this precocious, young science—but the future appears no less exciting. There is the genetics of mitochondria and other cytoplasmic elements to solve. The genetic control of membrane structure and function has hardly been touched. The tools of molecular genetics are only now being focused on the big problems of biological differentiation, the molecular basis of memory, and the genetics of behavior.

Although the goals of genetics are far from modest, progress in this science, as in all sciences, is made in modest steps by modest (and some not so modest) men. Therein lies the personal excitement of research— an experiment designed with imagination, carried out with precision, culminating (at least occasionally) in new concepts. It is with these current concepts of genetics that this book is concerned.

I have faced the same space dilemma that J. D. Watson acknowledges in his outstanding book titled *Molecular Biology of the Gene*. My aim has been to retain the rigor the discipline deserves within the space allocated.

Special recognition is due all my colleagues who have made this field so continuously exciting through their published works. In addition, I want to acknowledge that unique contribution made by my students—graduate and undergraduate, both past and present.

A. G. DeB.

Contents

DNA: The Primary Genetic Material

BIOLOGICAL SYSTEMS employ large polymeric molecules for storage of genetic information. With few exceptions, the nucleic acid DNA (deoxyribonucleic acid) serves as the primary genetic material.

Nucleic acids were isolated almost one hundred years ago, and although DNA was recognized as a component of chromosomes about seventy years ago, direct experimental evidence for its genetic role was presented only within the past twenty-five years. It was just in the middle 1950s that two different but related lines of study revealed unique structural characteristics on which many of our present concepts rest. We shall describe both the structural features of this informational macromolecule and the mechanism by which it is replicated for distribution to progeny. Later chapters will deal with its transcription (to RNA) and expression (in protein structure), as well as the recombination processes inherent in sexually reproducing organisms.

DNA Structure

Although DNA is physically a very large molecule with a molecular weight of several million, it consists chemically of monomers called *nucleotides*. Each nucleotide contains phosphoric acid, a five-carbon sugar (deoxyribose), and one of four kinds of nitrogenous bases (Figure 1·1). Two bases are purines (adenine and guanine) and two bases are pyrimidines (thymine and cytosine). When a purine (or pyrimidine) base is linked to the deoxyribose sugar, the unit is called a *nucleoside*. The phosphate is in turn attached to the sugar by an ester linkage and it is this nucleotide unit that is the fundamental building block of DNA. Thus, DNA as isolated is a large polymer con-

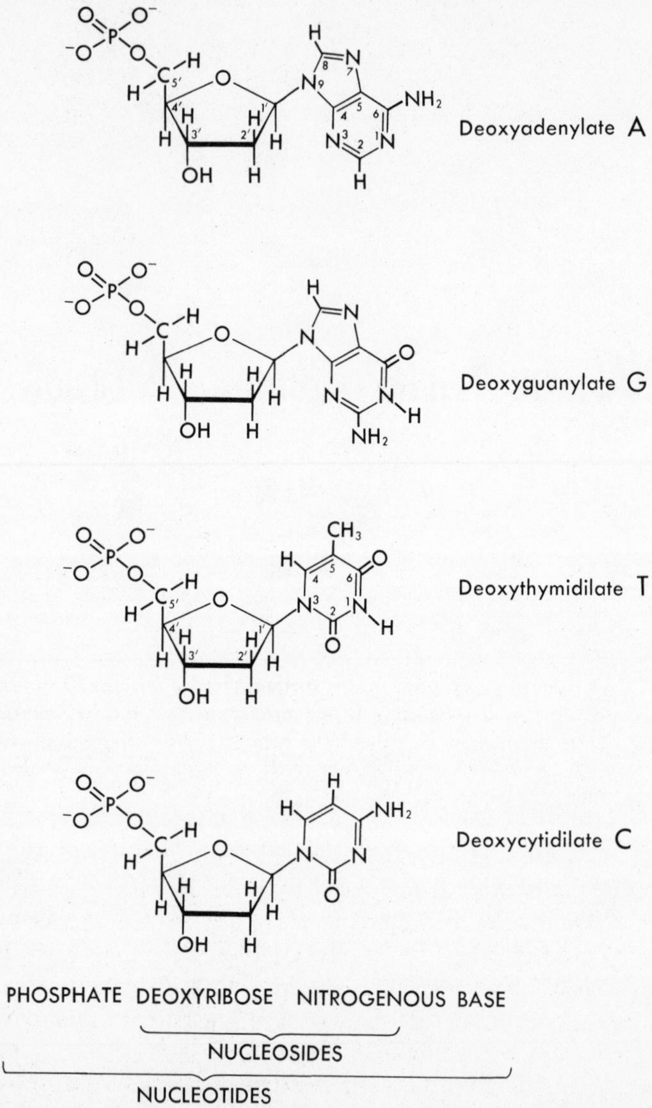

Deoxyadenylate A

Deoxyguanylate G

Deoxythymidilate T

Deoxycytidilate C

PHOSPHATE DEOXYRIBOSE NITROGENOUS BASE

NUCLEOSIDES

NUCLEOTIDES

Figure 1·1. The four nucleotides of DNA. Four different kinds of nitrogenous bases occur in DNA. Two are purines (A, G) and two are pyrimidines (T, C). Bonding occurs between the bases and a deoxyribose sugar to form a nucleoside. The further addition of a phosphate to the sugar results in a nucleotide, the fundamental unit of DNA structure.

sisting of a long chain of some 200,000 nucleotides called a *poly-nucleotide*.

Chemical analysis revealed three fundamental features of DNA structure: (1) Regardless of the source, DNA contains equivalent

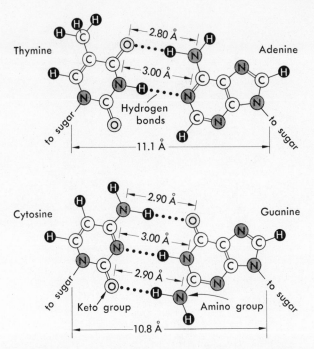

Figure 1·2. Association of base pairs through hydrogen bonding. Positioning of a purine relative to a pyrimidine in the arrangements indicated allows sharing of hydrogens between two bases. It should be noted that keto (oxygen) groups always match with amino (nitrogen) groups. [After J. D. Watson, *Molecular Biology of the Gene*, New York: W. A. Benjamin, Inc., 1965, p. 132.]

amounts of purines and pyrimidines. (2) There is further equivalence between the amounts of adenine (A) and thymine (T) as well as between guanine (G) and cytosine (C); i.e., A = T and G = C. (3) The *base ratio* of (A + T)/(G + C), therefore, may vary but is a constant value for a particular species. DNA from a particular organism may contain only 25 percent A + T whereas other DNA from another organism may contain 25 percent G + C.

Thus, chemical analysis suggests that some unusual relationship exists between particular bases that accounts for the observed ratios. These observations coupled with the x-ray diffraction studies of Wilkins led to a proposal for the structure of DNA by J. D. Watson (an American biologist) and F. H. C. Crick (an English chemist). The essential features of x-ray diffraction analysis suggested that the purine and pyrimidine bases (which are flat) are arranged at right angles to the long axis of the polynucleotide chain and are stacked one above the other. The chain is not straight but helical in shape and probably consists of at least two associated chains.

The model that now bears the name of its authors still continues to

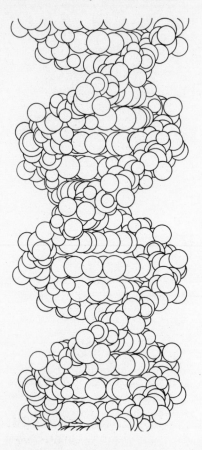

Figure 1·3. A molecular model of double-helical DNA. [After A. R. Stokes, in *Nature, 175:680, 1955.*]

have a phenomenal impact on almost all our concepts of modern genetics. The unique feature of the Watson-Crick model was the association of A—T and G—C into nucleotide base pairs through *hydrogen bonding* (Figure 1·2). A hydrogen bond is individually very weak but through the cooperative strength of the thousands in a single DNA molecule, the two chains are held tightly and precisely oriented, one to the other.

The particular pairing of a purine with pyrimidine occurs because of a perfect match between hydrogen donor and hydrogen acceptor sites on the two molecules. Thus, at least in the normal DNA molecule, adenine and thymine share two hydrogen bonds and guanine and cytosine share three hydrogen bonds. Such a purine-pyrimidine relationship is further supported by the observed constant diameter of DNA, which would not be possible if two large purines were paired.

DNA then consists of two chains (Figure 1·3) twisted around each other in a regular fashion, requiring about ten nucleotide base pairs for each complete turn of a double helix. The nitrogen bases (purines

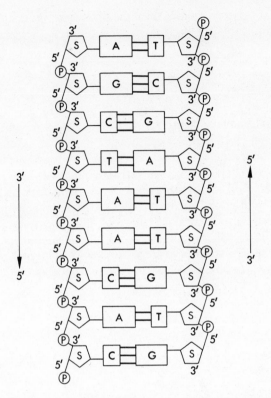

Figure 1·4. Diagram of the DNA double helix. Specific base pairing occurs (A-T; G-C); the two strands are not identical but complementary and are held together through hydrogen bonding of (complementary) bases. The 3'-5'-phosphodiester linkages are in reverse order in the two chains.

and pyrimidines) face into the middle of the helix with the sugars and phosphate backbone surrounding them. The distance between bases is 3.4 Å and the diameter of the molecule is about 20 Å.

Both chemical and physical data place severe restrictions on the structure of DNA in terms of shape and relationship between bases as well as chains. However, no restriction is placed on the *sequence* of bases (or base pairs) along the length of the molecule. Therefore, although the molecule is simple in composition (and even in shape), there is almost unlimited variability in possible sequence of bases and sets of bases. We shall see in later chapters that, indeed, information is stored in base sequence and such relationships form the basis for the genetic code.

It is to be noted, in particular, that the two strands comprising the double helix are *not identical* but instead are *complementary* (Figure 1·4). Furthermore, the chains run in opposite directions in terms of attachments between sugars through phosphate groups. We shall see later the implication of both these facts in terms of replication of the molecule.

DNA Replication

In their model, Watson and Crick proposed a mechanism by which replication of DNA might occur. Advantage was taken of both the complementary nature of the two chains and base-pairing specificity. They suggested that the two strands separate (we shall call one Watson and the other Crick), thus making available free hydrogen bonds for pairing with complementary bases. As this "unzipping" and base-pairing process proceeds along the molecule, two new molecules are formed; Watson has formed a new and complementary Crick, and in turn Crick should form a new Watson. Two daughter molecules result that have the same nucleotide base sequence as the original molecule (Figure 1·5).

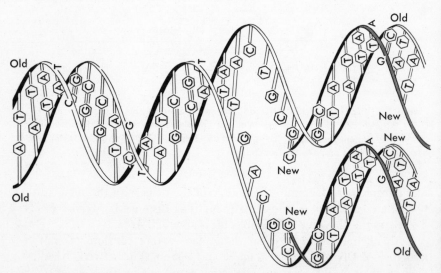

Figure 1·5. Replication of DNA. Replication is assumed to occur by sequential unzipping of the double helix. The new nucleotides are positioned (by an enzyme) and phosphate bridges formed, thus restoring the original double-helical configuration. Each newly formed double-helix consists of one old strand and one new strand. [After Watson, *Molecular Biology of the Gene*, New York: W. A. Benjamin, Inc., 1965, p. 207.]

If such a model is correct, it would require that each daughter molecule be half old and half new. Such a mode of replication has been termed *semiconservative*. This mode of replication proposed by Watson and Crick contrasts with *conservative* replication, which would result in an old (parental) molecule and a new (daughter) molecule (Figure 1·6). Several lines of experimentation with highly diverse organisms gave immediate support to the semiconservative model.

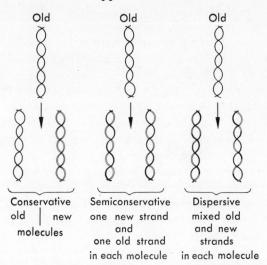

Figure 1·6. Three hypothetical models for the replication of DNA. (1) The conservative model would result in one completely new molecule and one old (template) molecule. Although some evidence exists for this model, it is not widely accepted. (2) The semiconservative model is that proposed by Watson and Crick and supported by the experiments of Taylor and Meselson and Stahl. (3) The dispersive mode of replication actually occurs to a limited extent during genetic repair and will be discussed in other chapters. [After Ingram, *The Biosynthesis of Macromolecules*, New York: W. A. Benjamin, Inc., 1965, p. 22.]

THE TAYLOR EXPERIMENTS

J. Herbert Taylor grew seedlings of the bean *Vicia faba* in solutions of radioactive thymidine, one of the nucleosides that is found exclusively in DNA. The root-tip cells incorporate the labeled thymidine into chromosomes that house the genetic material of higher plants and animals. These complex structures contain DNA and thus become labeled when they duplicate in the presence of radioactive thymidine.

After cells had been exposed to radioactive thymidine during the first chromosome duplication, they were transferred to nonradioactive thymidine. The new medium also contained colchicine, a chemical that prevents nuclear (and cell) division without affecting chromosome duplication. The number of chromosome divisions can thereby be determined directly by counting the number of chromosomes in a particular cell. Cells are fixed to microscope slides in such a way that individual chromosomes can be seen. The radioactive label in the chromosomes can be followed by means of a photographic emulsion that covers the mounted cells. Such an emulsion is sensitive to the radioactivity and becomes exposed in a minute region called an exposure grain. Thus, not only can the number of chromosome replications be determined but, by following the distribution of exposure grains, the distribution of labeled DNA can be followed in daughter chromosomes.

Both daughter chromosomes were uniformly labeled after one cycle of duplication in the nonradioactive medium. This would suggest that replication does not result in an old and a new chromosome. If this were true, only one daughter chromosome would be labeled.

Another set of cells was allowed to undergo two full cycles of duplication. Only half the chromosomes were labeled with thymidine. These experiments suggest that each chromosome is composed of two subunits, each of which replicate and segregate at each division stage. If we consider these observations in light of the Watson-Crick model, we might suppose the chromosome to contain two DNA strands that separate during chromosome division in a semiconservative manner. Each new molecule would still contain label after a single replication (as the chromosomes in Taylor's experiment). However, since only one strand contains radioactive material when the molecule replicates again (by strand separation), one labeled and one unlabeled daughter molecule result. Again, this corresponds to Taylor's observation with replicating chromosomes.

THE MESELSON-STAHL EXPERIMENT

Experiments equally elegant as those of Taylor were carried out with the bacterium *Escherichia coli* by M. S. Meselson and F. W. Stahl (Figure 1·7). They used a technique called *equilibrium density-gradient centrifugation*, which makes it possible to separate molecules of DNA that differ only in their isotope composition. DNA is mixed with a solution of cesium chloride and centrifuged at high speed for long periods of time. Molecules of differing densities eventually separate into narrow bands corresponding to the position in the centrifuge tube at which the DNA has the same density as that of cesium chloride. In this way molecules that differ only in that one contains heavy ^{15}N isotope-labeled nitrogen and the other is composed of the ordinary light (^{14}N) nitrogen can be separated and photographed as separate bands in the centrifuge tube.

Meselson and Stahl grew bacterial cells for several generations in medium containing ^{15}N-labeled ammonium chloride as a nitrogen source. Ordinary ^{14}N ammonium chloride was added to the cultures; at various time intervals, cell samples were removed and the DNA extracted from each sample.

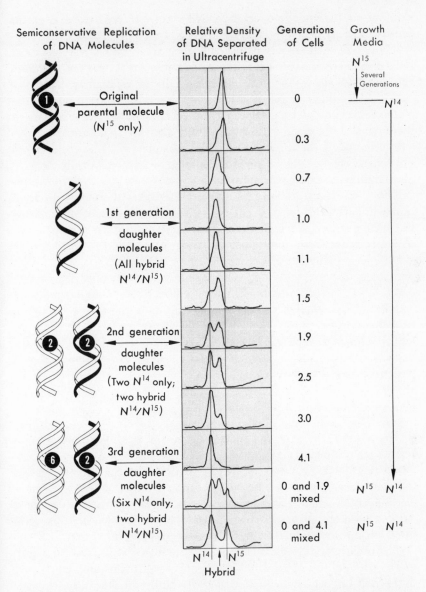

Figure 1·7. The Meselson-Stahl experiment. The photographs represent the banding of DNA in the centrifuge cell. Tracings of these photographs are on the right. Interpretation of the experiment is represented as double-helix molecules after various generations. [After Meselson and Stahl, in *Proc. Natl. Acad. Sci., 44:675, 1958.*]

Successive samples represented various stages in the replication of DNA and the transition of ^{15}N- to ^{14}N-containing molecules. Each sample, of course, consisted of many cells; therefore the DNA represented a population of molecules which were subjected to equilibrium density-gradient centrifugation.

By the end of one population cell generation, the DNA has been fully converted to a less dense form—but its density was *intermediate* between fully heavy (^{15}N) and fully light (^{14}N) samples used as standards. In other words, a hybrid intermediate stage represented the molecules produced by daughter cells. At the end of two generations there occurs about equal amounts of a light (^{14}N) band and this hybrid band. At the third generation, about one-fourth of the DNA is still hybrid. Hybrid DNA remains as long as it is technically possible quantitatively to compare the two types.

These results, as do Taylor's, support the semiconservative mode of replication of DNA that would require an intermediate, half-labeled stage, each strand of which would (in the absence of isotope) give rise to unlabeled as well as hybrid progeny molecules.

THE CAIRNS EXPERIMENT

John Cairns carried out a number of experiments that were, in principle, similar to those of Taylor. They were, however, carried out with the bacterium *E. coli,* which has no visible chromosome. On the basis of genetic evidence (see Chapter 6), the genes in bacteria are all present within a single linkage group. Cairns demonstrated that the chromosome of *E. coli* consists of a single molecule of DNA that has about six million nucleotide bases. This is the largest single molecule known to occur in a biological system.

The experiment involved pulse labeling of a replicating chromosome with radioactive thymidine, which is incorporated into DNA. The cell is gently broken open by enzymatic treatment and the (hopefully) unbroken DNA molecule extracted. By special technique it is carefully mounted on a photographic emulsion for autoradiography. The radioisotope in newly formed DNA slowly exposes the film, producing a diffuse profile of the DNA molecule (Figure 1·8).

The molecule is duplicated at a single site that traverses the length of the chromosome (molecule). This site is called the *replicating fork* —the point at which two chains become four. Furthermore, the two original chains are distributed to both newly synthesized chains in a manner consistent with semiconservative replication. That is, only one strand of the DNA molecule is labeled after the first replication and both may be labeled after the second and subsequent replications.

Enzymatic Synthesis of DNA in Vitro

It has long been the hope of both the biochemist and the geneticist to synthesize genetic material in the test tube. This end appeared to be

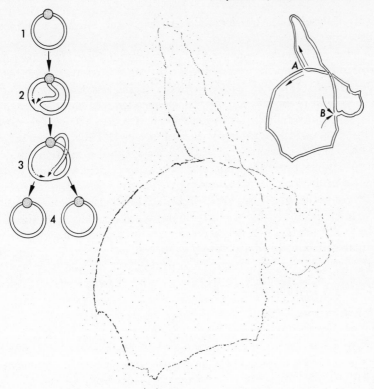

Figure 1·8. The Cairns experiment. The *E. coli* chromosome exists as a circular structure. Replication proceeds from a common initiation point resulting in two new circles of DNA (*left*). The replicating chromosome is labeled fully with thymidine (H^3) and the second replication allowed to begin in the presence of the same label. The large figure is an autoradiograph of the chromosome halfway through replication. Dense segments (to the left of *A*) represent doubly labeled DNA duplexes. Weakly labeled segments represent singly labeled DNA molecules. *B* (insert) represents the first point replicated; *A* represents the replication point where last synthesis has occurred. [After Cairns, in *Cold Spring Harbor Laboratory of Quantitative Biology,* 28:43, 1963.]

in sight when A. Kornberg isolated and purified an enzyme (DNA polymerase), that, with appropriate additional requirements, yielded a DNA-like molecule having almost identical physical and chemical properties as that of native DNA. The fact that the DNA-like polymer produced did not have biological activity does not distract from its potential significance; Kornberg, along with S. Ochoa (who discovered a similar RNA synthetic enzyme), received the Nobel prize for his discoveries.

Kornberg's enzyme, DNA polymerase, required several components. All *four* deoxyribonucleoside triphosphates must be present along with a primer DNA of high molecular weight. Approximately twenty times the amount of primer DNA originally present is produced until one of the nucleoside triphosphates is exhausted. When one of these components is missing, very little synthesis occurs and that which does probably involves addition of growing nucleotides to the ends of the primer chain. No synthesis at all occurs if the primer DNA is omitted. DNA from any source will serve as a primer, but it is far more efficient if it is denatured so as to separate the two strands. This would suggest that synthesis occurs by a process involving base pairing that would be expected to produce a DNA product complementary with the primer. Indeed, the base ratio is equal to that of primer DNA. To test the possibility that such a ratio was only fortuitous, Josse, a coworker of Kornberg, devised an ingenious technique called *nearest-neighbor sequence analysis.* This technique allowed an estimate of the relative frequencies with which pairs of nucleotides lie next to each other. Such neighbor frequencies could be compared between primer and product. When such comparisons were made, the correspondence was remarkable. Furthermore, the method showed that synthesis proceeded in opposite directions along each of the two strands of primer DNA. This would, of course, suggest that synthesis occurs from opposite ends of the double helix or that a separate (and as yet undiscovered) enzyme exists that is specific for synthesis in the opposite direction. Other experiments performed by Cairns suggest that both chains replicate in the same direction, so we are left with the problem of parallel growth of two antiparallel chains.

As mentioned earlier, the product DNA is similar in physical properties to primer. The sedimentation constant and viscosity are similar and the estimated molecular weight of product DNA may be as high as six times 10^6. However, Kornberg has observed unusual branched structures in synthetic DNA. This observation may provide an explanation of the lack of biological activity. For example, it is possible that occasionally the enzyme crosses over and starts to copy the partner strand in the opposite direction. This would give rise to an incomplete molecule in terms of biological information, but proper base ratios and neighbor frequencies would be represented in a large population of such product molecules.

All these findings suggest that if the enzyme is really responsible for DNA synthesis in vivo, it must operate under very restricted conditions and thus avoid the high level of mistakes that characterize its action in the test tube.

DNA as Genetic Material

For a number of years it has become increasingly clear that DNA is the genetic material. Chromosomes contain large amounts of DNA that remain constant from cell to cell, whereas both protein and RNA vary quantitatively. Haploid cells (e.g., sperm or eggs) contain only half as much DNA as that present in diploid cells of the same species. Furthermore, agents that react chemically or physically with DNA (such as ultraviolet light, which is absorbed by nucleic acids) are also highly mutagenic.

However, two studies—one with bacteria and the other with a bacterial virus (bacteriophage)—provide particularly compelling evidence that DNA is the primary genetic material.

GENETIC TRANSFORMATION

Transformation studies date back to 1928, when F. Griffith (in England) performed a series of experiments with the bacterium *Diplococcus pneumoniae,* which causes pneumonia. Certain strains of pneumococcus are not virulent and do not cause death when injected into mice. The virulent strains are characterized by a capsule of polysaccharide which is missing in the avirulent strains. Both cell lines are reasonably stable except for occasional mutations.

Griffith's startling discovery was made when he carried out a series of experiments injecting mice with heat-killed bacteria (Figure 1·9). The injected mice were not infected by the virulent strain when it had been killed prior to injection by heating the cells to 60°C. However, when these dead cells were injected along with live cells of the harmless strain, the mice frequently died. Furthermore, live virulent bacteria could be recovered from the dead mice. These transformed bacteria were quite stable and could be used to repeat the experiment.

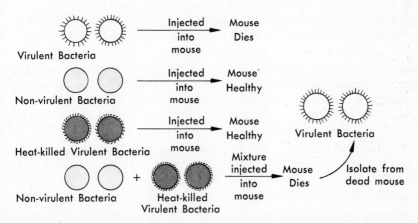

Figure 1·9. Genetic transformation of bacteria. The virulent principle is transferred from dead cells into live nonvirulent cells. The transformed bacteria are virulent and kill the mouse. [After Bonner, *Heredity,* Englewood Cliffs: Prentice-Hall, Inc., 1961, p. 10.]

Further experiments were performed that showed that some factor from the heat-killed cells was responsible for the transformation. Experiments were eventually performed outside the mice, using standard microbiological culturing procedures in broth and on agar petri dishes.

It was not until 1944 that three workers, Avery, MacLeod, and McCarty, performed the crucial experiment of fractionating the dead cells to identify the chemical responsible for transformation. There were at that time several candidates for the genetic material: it might have been a carbohydrate—the virulent cells had a polysaccharide capsule; it might have been a protein—proteins are very large and complicated molecules and were known to be associated with chromosomes of higher organisms. Perhaps the least likely component was the nucleic acid—many workers felt it to be too simple a molecule to store all the genetic information. As you already know, it was proved beyond doubt that the genetic material transferred from the dead to the live cells was DNA. The final crushing blow to the protein proponents was the demonstration that an enzyme that destroys DNA (DNase) rapidly inactivated the transformation material. Enzymes destroying RNA (RNase) and protein (proteases) are without effect on the genetic material.

In recent years much has been learned concerning the transfer of DNA into recipient cells and these transformation studies will be discussed in a later section involving recombination.

THE HERSHEY-CHASE EXPERIMENT

A classic experiment now bearing the name of A. D. Hershey and Martha C. Chase was performed with bacteriophage in the early 1950s. The phage T_2 grows inside the cells of *E. coli* until the cell bursts, releasing several hundred new phage. T_2 are neat, small, tadpole-shaped structures consisting of a head comprised of a protein coat surrounding DNA and a tail through which attachment occurs to the infected cell. About equal parts of DNA and protein compose the total phage.

Two kinds of phage particles were prepared: one was grown in bacteria containing radioactive sulfur (^{35}S), the other in bacteria containing radioactive phosphorus (^{32}P). The ^{35}S-labeled phage contained radioactivity exclusively in the amino acid constituting the protein of phage. The phage grown in ^{32}P bacteria contained the radioactivity in the DNA of the progeny phage. Each was used independently to infect bacteria. A brief treatment with an electric blender shortly after the bacteria were infected broke the loose attachment between the phage and the cell but had little effect on the number of infected bac-

teria. In other words, something was injected into the
contained the genetic information to make new, complet
Measurement of radioactivity in the bacteria dete
DNA or protein (or both) is injected. It was clear tha
the host cell almost exclusively and that it was suffici..
the construction of the complete phage structure. The protein
was discarded during the infective process, serving only as the vehicle
for injection of DNA into the host cell.

RNA as Primary Genetic Material

Although we are now confident that DNA is beyond doubt the primary genetic material of most organisms, exceptions have been found
among the viruses. All viruses contain nucleic acid but many of those
that infect higher plants contain RNA. Tobacco mosaic virus (TMV)
is the best-studied example of this type.

TMV is a simple rod-shaped virus consisting of an RNA core sur-
rounded by a protein coat. The two can be separated, one from the
other, and under certain conditions will reaggregate into infective-
virus particles indistinguishable from native TMV. Fraenkel-Conrat
and Williams took advantage of this ability of TMV to reaggregate in
an ingenious experiment that provided direct proof that RNA is the
genetic material for the virus.

Several related strains of TMV are known and can be distinguished
on the basis of infectivity and structure of the protein coat. The RNA
was separated from the protein in two different strains. The components could be allowed to aggregate in all combinations that included
hybrids composed of incorrect RNA-protein combinations. These
hybrids, when allowed to infect tobacco plants, provide a method by
which a distinction may be made as to whether RNA or protein determines the symptoms of the disease and the characteristics of the
progeny viruses. In both cases, RNA exerted exclusive control. Not
only was the infection characteristic of that strain from which the
RNA was derived but also all progeny were identical with the original
strain donating the RNA to the hybrid. The protein had contributed
in no way to the character of the progeny. The RNA contains all
hereditary information necessary for the production of more virus.

References

Borek, Ernest. *The Code of Life,* New York: Columbia, 1965.
Barry, J. M. *Genes and the Chemical Control of Living Cells,* Englewood
Cliffs, N.J.: Prentice-Hall, 1964.

Davidson, J. N. *The Biochemistry of the Nucleic Acids,* New York: Wiley, 1960.

Hayes, William. *The Genetics of Bacteria and Their Viruses,* New York: Wiley, 1964.

Ingram, Vernon M. *The Biosynthesis of Macromolecules,* New York: W. A. Benjamin, Inc., 1965.

Kornberg, A. *Enzymatic Synthesis of DNA,* New York: Wiley, 1962.

Peacocke, A. R., and R. B. Drysdale. *The Molecular Basis of Heredity,* London: Butterworth, 1965.

Potter, Van R. *Nucleic Acid Outlines: Structure and Metabolism,* Minneapolis: Burgess, 1960.

Stahl, Franklin W. *The Mechanics of Inheritance,* Englewood Cliffs, N.J.: Prentice-Hall, 1965.

Strauss, Bernard S. *Chemical Genetics,* Philadelphia: Saunders, 1960.

Watson, J. D. *Molecular Biology of the Gene,* New York: W. A. Benjamin, Inc., 1965.

Genetic Transcription and Translation: The Role of the RNAs in Protein Synthesis

THE MYRIAD NUMBER of organisms that exist in nature are delineated mainly by differences in proteins. DNA exerts its control principally by specifying the synthesis of particular protein molecules. RNA (ribonucleic acid) plays a central role in this highly regulated process. The overall pattern of information flow from DNA may be summarized as follows:

Replication   Transcription   Translation

$$\text{DNA} \longrightarrow \text{RNA} \longrightarrow \text{Protein}$$

RNA occurs as three major types—messenger-RNA, ribosomal-RNA, and transfer-RNA. Each type has its own unique function in the transcription of information from DNA and in its translation to protein structure, but all have many structural features in common.

RNA Structure

The chemical composition of RNA is quite similar to that of DNA; this similarity is meaningful in terms of information translation in the cell. RNA differs from DNA in only three essential ways: the ribose sugar; the pyrimidine base, uracil; and the single-stranded nature of RNA polymers.

The components of RNA (Figure 2·1) have been deduced (as with DNA) by examination of the products of extensive chemical and enzymatic hydrolysis. In RNA, the nucleotides contain a ribose sugar rather than the related deoxyribose of DNA. (The deoxyribose has one less oxygen in the 2′ position.) The ribose would normally occur following alkali hydrolysis as a 3′-monophosphate, that is, with a

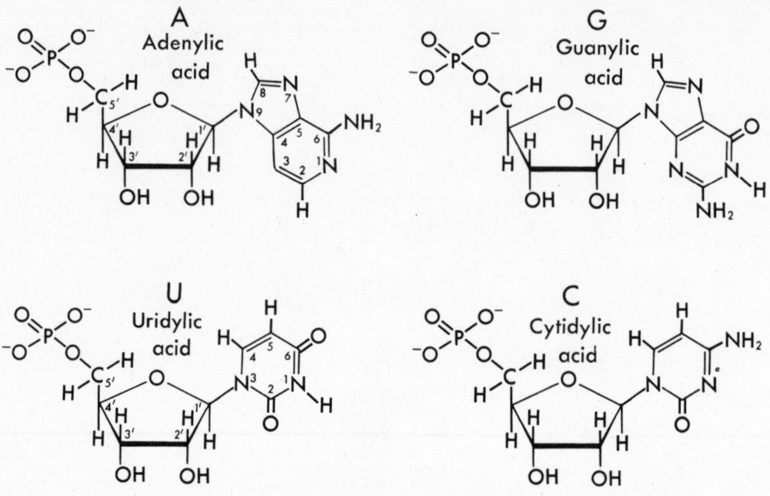

Figure 2·1. The nucleotide subunits of RNA. RNA differs from DNA in that it contains uracil instead of thymine and ribose instead of deoxyribose.

phosphate attached to the 3′ position of the ribose sugar. Certain enzymes (e.g., snake-venom diesterase) yield ribonucleoside-5′-monophosphate as a result of the cleavage of the phosphodiester bond in an alternative position. These observations suggest that RNA exists, as does DNA, in long chains with a phosphate backbone connected by means of a 3′-5′ linkage.

For the most part, RNA nucleotides consist of four bases, three of which are common to DNA (A,G,C) and the fourth, uracil (U), a substitute for the thymine of DNA. Thus, there occur the two purine bases, adenine and guanine, and the two pyrimidine bases, cytosine and uracil. Certain rare bases such as methylated purines occur in RNA and special enzymes exist for their formation, probably in the completed polymer.

The purine-pyrimidine ratio of RNA is not 1:1, as it is in the case of DNA. This suggests that the molecule exists as a single strand consisting of a string of ribonucleosides (base-sugars) attached through 3′-5′-phosphoribose linkages. Thus it is similar in many respects to a single unbranched strand (half-helix) of DNA.

The absence of regular hydrogen bonding results in an irregular (and uncertain) secondary structure. X-ray diffraction and other physical studies, however, suggest regions of helical double-stranded structure. These probably exist because of loops in which a single strand bends back upon itself. Such an arrangement would result from hydrogen bonding between A—U and G—C but such matched regions must be limited in extent.

The unique feature of the DNA molecule in terms of information storage is the sequence of bases that may occur in an infinite variety of patterns. That a similar potential for information storage exists in RNA suggests its possible role as an intermediate in information transfer. Furthermore, the resemblance of RNA to one strand of the double-stranded DNA suggests a mechanism for transcription of base sequence between the two molecules. The process probably involves

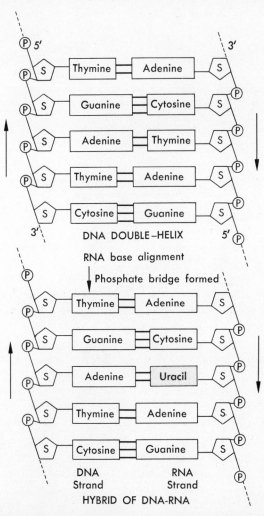

Figure 2·2. Hybrid of DNA and RNA. One strand of the DNA double-helix is used as a template for alignment of RNA bases. Once a base is in position, a phosphate bridge is formed between bases—resulting in a single strand of RNA. The hybrid thus contains one strand of DNA and one strand of RNA.

hydrogen bond–directed pairing between complementary bases (A—U, G—C) resulting in a hybrid molecule consisting of one strand containing DNA nucleotides and one strand containing RNA nucleotides (Figure 2·2). The transcribed RNA strand would therefore be complementary to but not identical to its DNA template strand.

ENZYMATIC SYNTHESIS OF RNA

Evidence for the relationship between template DNA and transcribed RNA came from the discovery of an enzyme capable of cata-

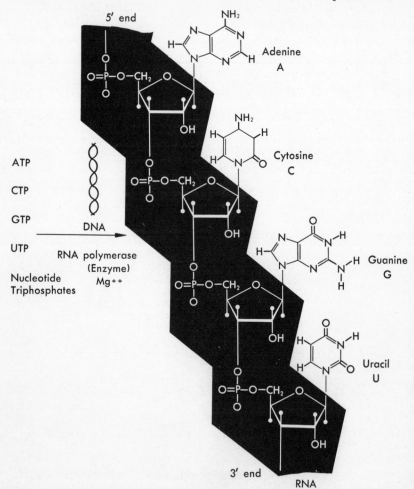

Figure 2·3. Enzymatic synthesis of RNA. The four ribonucleoside triphosphates are the building blocks of RNA. An enzyme (polymerase) as well as a magnesium ion is required. However, RNA synthesis does not occur without the presence of template DNA.

lyzing the formation of polymers of RNA. A requirement exists for the simultaneous presence of the four ribonucleoside triphosphates— ATP, GTP, CTP, and UTP—as well as a divalent ion such as magnesium. This enzyme, RNA polymerase, is similar to the DNA polymerases described by Kornberg, but it is unique in its requirement for template DNA (Figure 2·3). Thus, RNA will not serve as a template for its own synthesis—as did DNA and the Kornberg enzyme.

MESSENGER RNA (mRNA)

Studies by Hershey (and later by Volkin and Astrachan) with T_2 bacteriophage-infected (bacterial virus) *E. coli* led in 1956 to the first evidence for a unique kind of RNA, later to be called *messenger RNA*. They observed (by ^{32}P-labeling techniques) that following infection, the RNA formed was similar in base ratio (with U substituted for T) to that of the phage DNA—but unlike either the DNA of the host bacteria or the bulk RNA.

A variety of more recent studies have shown that the formation of mRNA is not unique to infected cells but constitutes 2 to 4 percent of the total RNA of normal cells. It can be recognized and its fate followed particularly well if a short (thirty seconds) pulse of radioactive ^{32}P is supplied to growing cells, then removed and "chased" by cold (nonradioactive) phosphorus. Following synthesis on the DNA template, mRNA appears to be associated with a single ribosome, then several ribosomes (polysomes), that are the sites of protein synthesis.

Messenger RNA is markedly unstable in bacterial systems but far more stable in higher organisms. This characteristic of rapid turnover plays an important role in genetic regulation. If mRNA serves as an intermediate in information transfer from DNA, its rate of formation and breakdown can impose a subtle mode of control on the expression of particular genes.

When DNA is heated, the two strands of the double-helix uncoil and separate. If the mixture is allowed to cool very slowly, the complementary strands reassociate by hydrogen bonding into the original double-helix. Spiegelman has taken advantage of this "renaturation" phenomenon to show that mRNA has not only the same ratio as DNA but also precisely the same *sequence* of bases as one of the strands of DNA. If melted, DNA is slowly cooled in the presence of mRNA and hybrid molecules of DNA-RNA are formed. This suggests that mRNA is identical in base sequence (except for U for T) to one DNA strand and is complementary to its partner strand.

In summary, it appears that mRNA is templated from one strand of the double-stranded DNA and this process clearly precedes protein synthesis, which occurs after mRNA is associated with a ribosome.

When the RNA products are analyzed, it is clear that the RNA base composition reflects the base composition of the DNA used as template. In other words, the AU/GC ratio of RNA is similar to the AT/GC ratio of the DNA product of enzymatic synthesis. Furthermore, when nearest-neighbor frequencies (see Chapter 1) are determined for both template DNA and product RNA, they proved to be complementary. This is consistent with the role of DNA in specifying by hydrogen bonding the linear array of bases in the RNA.

Both single-stranded and double-stranded DNA will serve as template for RNA polymerase in vitro. However, all evidence suggests that only one DNA strand acts as a template in vivo. Otherwise, two kinds of RNA would be formed for every sequence along the DNA molecule. This does not appear to be the case, but the mechanism for strand selection is unknown.

Translation from Messenger RNA to Protein

The control of protein synthesis is crucial to genetic regulation. Genes ultimately express themselves through proteins, the synthesis of which they direct. Central to this process is the translation of information coded in mRNA into the sequence of amino acids present in protein. Aside from mRNA, two other types of RNA participate in this process. They are ribosomal RNA (rRNA) and transfer RNA (tRNA). Recently determined evidence indicates that both rRNA and tRNA are made on DNA templates but differ markedly in method and rate of turnover. Although these two RNA types together constitute 96 to 98 percent of all RNA, they are templated from a small portion of the total DNA.

RIBOSOMAL RNA (rRNA)

Ribosomal RNA constitutes the bulk of the cellular RNA. It occurs in organized structures called ribosomes, which are nucleoprotein particles. In bacteria, ribosomes contain about 60 percent protein and 40 percent RNA. Ribosomes are the exclusive site of protein synthesis, but until recently we believed their only role was to orient the mRNA and tRNA. Each ribosome is quite large, with a molecular weight of near 3 million. They are constructed of two subunits, one having a molecular weight of 1.8 million and the smaller about half that weight (0.9 million). Ribosomes and their subunits are often described in terms of Svedberg units (S), which are a measure of the speed at which a particle sediments in the ultracentrifuge (Figure 2·4). The two subunits mentioned above are 30 S and 50 S; in combination they have a sedimentation constant of 70 S. The large 70-S ribosome falls

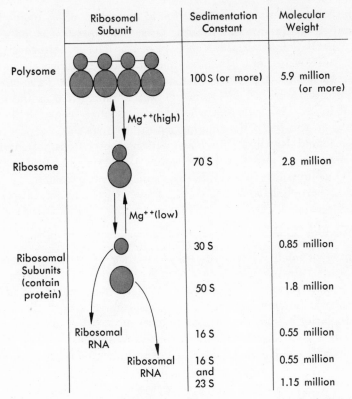

Ribosomal Subunit	Sedimentation Constant	Molecular Weight
Polysome	100 S (or more)	5.9 million (or more)
Mg++(high)		
Ribosome	70 S	2.8 million
Mg++(low)		
Ribosomal Subunits (contain protein)	30 S	0.85 million
	50 S	1.8 million
Ribosomal RNA	16 S	0.55 million
Ribosomal RNA	16 S and 23 S	0.55 million / 1.15 million

Figure 2·4. The subunits of ribosomes. [After Hartman and Suskind, *Gene Action*, Englewood Cliffs: Prentice-Hall, Inc., 1965, p. 34.]

apart when the Mg^{++} concentration is reduced. Both subunits contrain both protein and RNA. Their further dissociation results in 16S and 23S rRNA units, which are probably the fundamental ribosomal structural units. It should be noted that somewhat larger units of 18 S and 28 S are characteristic of fungi and higher organisms.

The functional ribosome as mentioned above contains a large amount of protein. Over thirty different proteins have been identified in ribosomes. That they serve specific functions is shown by the fact that loss of certain of the proteins results in loss of particular functional activity of the ribosome.

It has been postulated (though conflicting reports exist in the scientific literature) that ribosomal RNA may perform an mRNA-like function in the production of its own structural proteins, then fold up into completed ribosomes. It is known that the RNA from a completed ribosome cannot serve as a messenger, however. If nascent rRNA can serve such a role it must be altered (e.g., by the addition of methyl groups to certain bases) as the ribosome is constructed.

As mentioned earlier, mRNA is found associated with single ribosomes or groups of ribosomes during protein synthesis. The presence of RNA in ribosomes suggests some sort of base pairing. However, the precise function of both ribosomes and rRNA is unknown. There is some recent evidence that one of the subunits of rRNA serves to release the mRNA from DNA. The subunit would then lead the message out to a cytoplasmic site where the ribosome is completed, thus initiating protein synthesis. The mechanism by which all or part of a ribosome could function to release nascent message from template DNA is far from clear. Although much work remains to be done before ribosomes are fully understood, their central role in protein synthesis is beyond debate.

TRANSFER RNA (tRNA)

A group of small RNA molecules exists that serves as acceptors of amino acids, thus playing a key role in protein synthesis. At least one tRNA occurs for each of the twenty amino acids; and each tRNA has a slightly different structure. However, the tRNAs studied have great similarity in size, each containing seventy-five to eighty nucleotides with a total molecular weight of approximately 25,000. They occur as single chains, but a great deal of hydrogen bonding is present,

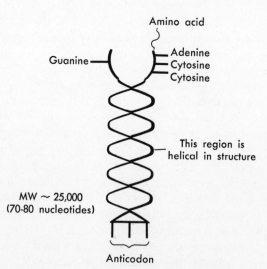

Figure 2·5. Diagrammatic representation of a tRNA molecule. The molecule is a single chain; but in folding back on itself, hydrogen bonds are formed and, in certain regions, the double-helical configuration is assumed. One end of the chain (3'-OH) always terminates with adenine, cytosine, and cytosine; the amino acid is attached to tRNA through the adenine. A guanine is always present on the opposite end of the chain.

presumably because the chain folds back on itself in a cloverleaf shape. These regions of base pairing resemble a DNA double-helix in that they assume a coiled configuration.

Another characteristic feature of tRNA is the chain endings, which are identical for all tRNA types (Figure 2·5). One chain end, with a 3′-hydroxyl group, always terminates with the three bases CCA. (The A is the site of amino acid attachment.) The other end of the chain (with a 5′-phosphate) terminates with G (guanylic acid).

Transfer RNA is unique in that it contains bases other than the four commonly found in RNA (A,U,G, and C). One such base is pseudouridylic acid, in which the ribose is attached to the 5-carbon of uracil rather than to the 3-nitrogen. A number of other unusual bases have additional methyl groups attached. Frequently, these methyl groups interfere with base pairing when they replace hydrogens involved in hydrogen bonding. Those regions of tRNA containing methylated bases could not exist as double-stranded regions and may, in fact, exist specifically to prevent such base pairing. These unusual bases are probably formed after the usual base sequences are laid down. How enzymes determine which base is to be methylated is far from clear.

Late in 1964, Holley performed the difficult analytical job of determining the nucleotide sequence of the particular tRNA in yeast that specifically binds the amino acid alanine. This tRNA has seventy-seven nucleotides and is characterized by the presence of several (nine) unusual bases (Figure 2·6). Until Holley's investigation, it was felt that the secondary configuration of tRNA would be obvious if the sequence was known. However, several alternative shapes are possible that allow a fair amount of hydrogen bonding.

Even though tRNA is the smallest of the nucleic acids, it plays a key role in protein synthesis. However, the need for three or four specific regions or sites in the molecule can now be recognized. One is the amino acid attachment site, which occurs on one end of the molecule and is the same for all tRNAs and consists of the base adenine (A). A site must exist by which the amino acid is attached to the correct tRNA through the action of a specific enzyme (synthetase). Such a site is called the *recognition site* and must match the enzyme in some way; otherwise tRNA would be charged with the wrong amino acid. A third site is the anticodon triplet of bases which is complementary with a triplet in mRNA. Presumably these bases would occur in the unpaired (single-stranded) region of the loop of tRNA. It is, of course, possible that the recognition site and the anticodon are identical. Finally, because tRNA is temporarily attached to the ribosome before growth of the peptide chain can occur, there probably exists a ribosome recognition site.

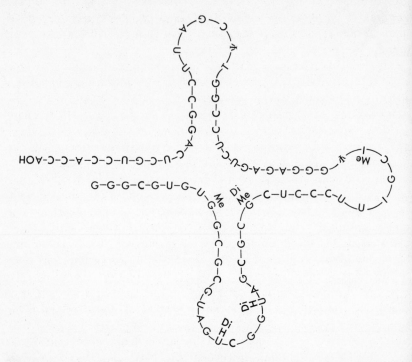

Figure 2·6. Primary structure of an alanyl tRNA. The actual configuration of this molecule is not known, although the nucleotide sequence is precise. Nine unusual bases are present in the molecule, which contains seventy-seven nucleotides. [From Holley, *Science 147*: 1462–1464, March 19, 1965. Copyright 1965 by the American Association for the Advancement of Science.]

Protein Synthesis: A Cellular View

Biochemical evidence suggests that both the secondary structure and, in turn, the function of proteins are direct consequences of the linear sequence of amino acids (or primary structure) in the polypeptide chains. For example, enzymes (the catalytic proteins) influence and control the various metabolic conversions of all cells. As we shall see in later chapters, gene mutations are usually reflected in protein structure and thus influence the function of the cell machinery.

PROTEIN STRUCTURE

Proteins are long-chain polymers of amino acids. About twenty different amino acids occur in proteins (Figure 2·7), and all have an asymmetric carbon that is joined by covalent bonds to four different groups—a carboxyl, an amino, a hydrogen, and an R group (Figure 2·8). The R groups are different for each amino acid, some of them being quite complicated. Amino acids are unusual in that they may act as either an acid or a base because of the presence of the carboxyl and amino groups.

Most proteins contain between 100 and 1,000 amino acids and have molecular weights from 10,000 to 100,000. Amino acids are linked by a covalent bond called a *peptide bond* between the amino (NH_2) group of one amino acid and the carboxyl $(COOH)$ group of another (Figure 2·8). Thus, a protein is really a polypeptide chain. In each polypeptide chain a free carboxyl always occurs on one end and a free amino on the other (the C-terminal and N-terminal ends).

The complete sequence of amino acids in a protein is difficult to determine and is known for only a few proteins. However, it is this sequence that is determined by the sequence of bases in the DNA and is thus of primary importance to geneticists. The amino acid sequence is referred to as the *primary protein structure*.

The spatial organization of proteins is an important consideration. The configuration of the polypeptide backbone refers to the *secondary structure* of protein. Almost all proteins exist in a helical configuration called an α-helix. This helix, just as in DNA, is stabilized by intramolecular hydrogen bonding and involves the C=O and N—H groups of the peptide chain. The α-helix configuration allows the minimum number of hydrogen bonds without distorting bond distances or bond angles. Thus an α-helix represents a highly ordered structure. Probably few perfect α-helical structures exist, for they would be rigid and rod-shaped. It is more likely that an intermittent ordered structure is characteristic of most proteins.

Tertiary structure refers to the topological pattern of the folded chain. The special organization in tertiary structure is stabilized by the side chains of the amino acid rather than by the peptide backbone. Disulfide bridges are major groups that determine the topology of a folded protein. However, hydrophobic bonds, electrostatic interactions, and hydrogen bonds all probably contribute to side-chain interactions. Thus, tertiary structure refers to the three-dimensional structure of proteins, which is particularly important in the biological function of certain molecules such as enzymes. It is this structure that is subject to loss of stability from heating, changes in pH, and the presence of various ions. Such alterations account for the extreme instability of enzymes.

A further important structural consideration in large complex proteins is *quaternary structure*. Often two or more polypeptide chains become associated into a complex macromolecule that is the biologically functional unit. Certain enzymes, molecules such as hemoglobin, and the structural proteins of cells are dependent for activity on quaternary structure.

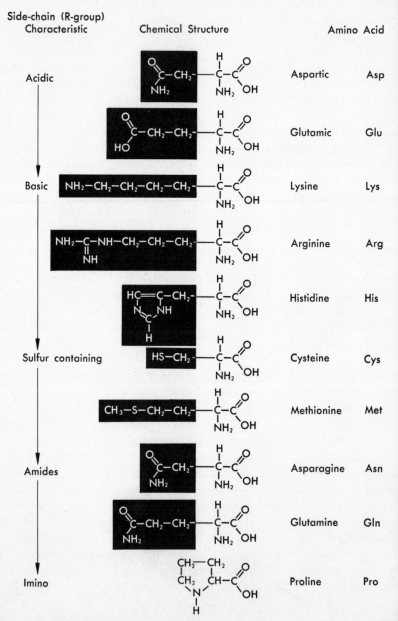

Side-chain (R-group)
Characteristic   Chemical Structure   Amino Acid

Figure 2·7. The amino acids found in proteins. The different side chains (R groups) on the different amino acids result in major differences in the chemical and physical properties of the amino acids as well as of the proteins formed from them. For example, the sulfhydryl (—SH) group present in cysteine is involved in the formation of disulfide bonds (S—S) found in proteins.

Side-chain (R-group) Characteristic	Chemical Structure	Amino Acid	
Aliphatic		Glycine	Gly
		Alanine	Ala
		Valine	Val
		Leucine	Leu
		Isoleucine	Ileu
Alcoholic		Serine	Ser
		Threonine	Thr
Aromatic		Tyrosine	Tyr
		Phenylalanine	Phe
		Tryptophan	Try

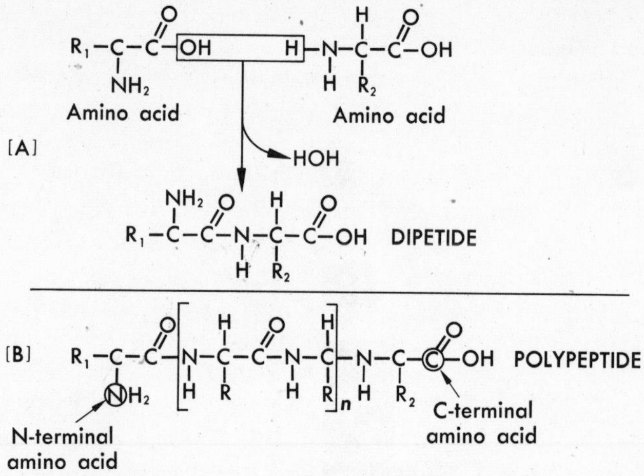

Figure 2·8. The formation of peptide bonds. The amino group (NH_2) of one amino acid and the carboxyl group (COOH) of another amino acid are involved in the formation of each peptide bond. A protein always has a free amino group at one end and a free carboxyl group at the other end of the unbranched molecule. During protein synthesis the N-terminal amino acid is positioned first and the C-terminal amino acid then joined. The growing tip of a peptide chain is the free carboxyl end.

PROTEIN BIOSYNTHESIS

THE ACTIVATION AND CHARGING REACTION. The initial step in protein biosynthesis consists of activation of amino acids by a reaction involving the energy-storage molecule, adenosine triphosphate (ATP). The carboxyl (COOH) group of the amino acid reacts with ATP and the product is aminoacyl adenylate with pyrophosphate released (Figure 2·9).

A large number of enzymes catalyze the activation, but each is specific for a particular amino acid. This means at least twenty enzymes must function at this step. Magnesium (as well as ATP) is involved in the reaction.

Enzyme-bound aminoacyl adenylate reacts immediately with transfer RNA (tRNA) giving an aminoacyl-tRNA product. The same enzyme that is involved in activation also functions to transfer the amino acid to tRNA. These enzymes are then called aminoacyl-tRNA synthetases. As catalysts they are unique because they not only activate the amino acid but must also be capable of recognizing a particular tRNA molecule. It is possible that structural changes in a particular synthetase might result in alteration of the coding relationships in that organism. Indeed, aminoacyl-tRNA synthetases are known to differ in diverse organisms. However, the level of mistakes is quite low—probably no more than one incorrect amino acid in several thousand transferred.

As mentioned earlier, tRNAs are small molecules consisting of only seventy-five to eighty bases. The amino acid is transferred to the adenine (A) that is present on one end of all tRNA molecules. The important match that must be met involves a unique triplet of bases in tRNA called the *anticodon*. The anticodon is complementary with a triplet (the codon) present in mRNA. If the incorrect amino acid becomes attached to a particular tRNA, that amino acid will be inserted into the growing peptide chain.

THE TRANSFER REACTION. Perhaps the most important step in protein synthesis is the transfer reaction. It involves aminoacyl-tRNA, ribosomes, and mRNA—resulting in peptide-bond formation. Two enzymes are required, as well as guanosine triphosphate (GTP) and several inorganic ions. Not only do the three major components interact but they do so in a dynamic way: mRNA moves in respect to the ribosomes; then tRNA molecules move in, become positioned, and enzyme interaction occurs.

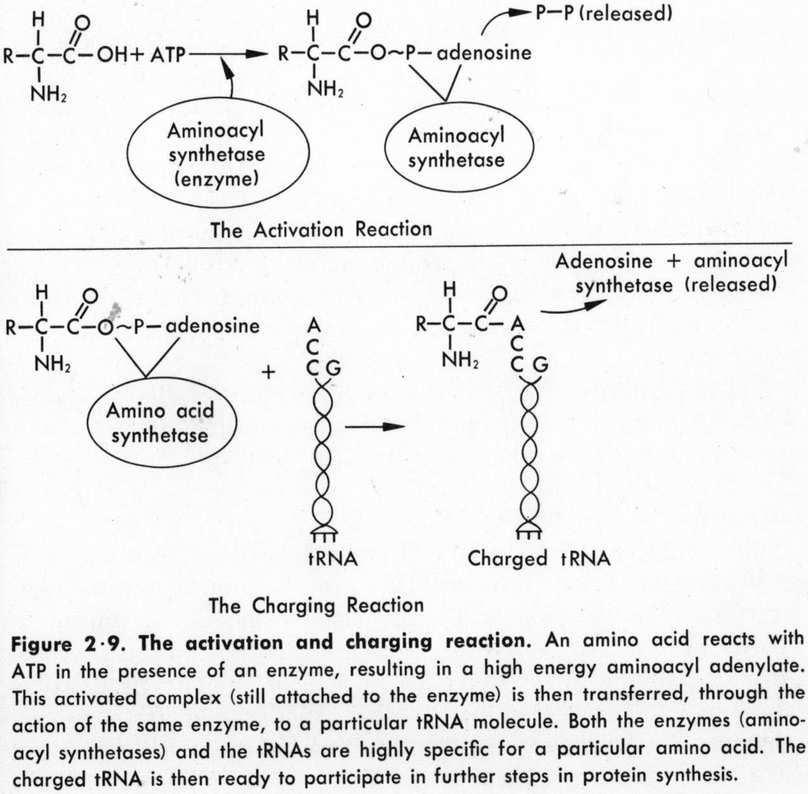

The Activation Reaction

The Charging Reaction

Figure 2·9. The activation and charging reaction. An amino acid reacts with ATP in the presence of an enzyme, resulting in a high energy aminoacyl adenylate. This activated complex (still attached to the enzyme) is then transferred, through the action of the same enzyme, to a particular tRNA molecule. Both the enzymes (aminoacyl synthetases) and the tRNAs are highly specific for a particular amino acid. The charged tRNA is then ready to participate in further steps in protein synthesis.

The first step in this process is the binding reaction between amino-acyl-tRNA and the mRNA-ribosome complex. It appears to be a nonenzymatic process, and both charged and uncharged tRNAs are bound. The binding is very specific, however, and has been employed for studies of the genetic code.

The attachment of the ribosome to the messenger is also quite specific and always occurs at a single site on the 5'-hydroxyl end of the mRNA. This corresponds to the position of the triplet coding for the N-terminal amino acid in the completed protein. Indeed, the attachment of ribosomes to mRNA may be rate limiting in protein synthesis.

Certain antibiotics (such as the tetracyclines) may inhibit protein synthesis by interfering with the binding reaction of the aminoacyl-tRNA. However, they do not appear to interfere with mRNA-ribosome attachment.

Two enzyme fractions function in peptide synthesis, one of which involves GTP. Only one tRNA can be bound for each ribosome in the absence of the enzyme fraction. However, when the enzyme is present, a second tRNA can be bound to the same ribosome. This suggests that the enzyme functions to modify the ribosome structure—producing a new binding site and moving the ribosome to the next codon on mRNA. At the same time, the peptidyl-RNA already attached to the ribosome is prepared to acylate the new aminoacyl-tRNA that is bound to the new site. Peptide-bond synthesis involves condensation of two aminoacyl-tRNAs to yield peptidyl-RNA and free RNA. Thus, the growing peptide chain is always attached to tRNA, which remains bound to the ribosome.

The antibiotic puromycin appears to replace aminoacyl-tRNA and to form a false peptide bond, resulting in chain termination. Thus, it stops protein synthesis and becomes the C-terminal of the released peptide chain. Release occurs because puromycin will not bind to the ribosome.

Still a third ribosome site has been proposed for the uncharged RNA that has just been released by peptide-bond formation. In summary, the three sites would be the decoding, condensing, and exit sites (Figure 2·10). Whether a particular site can serve any function through enzymatic action is unknown.

Still another antibiotic, Chloramphenicol, has long been known to be an inhibitor of protein synthesis. It appears to function in the transfer reaction at the step of peptide-bond synthesis. Attachment of mRNA to ribosomes seems to occur normally, but synthesis seldom proceeds past the di- or tripeptide stage. The inhibitor is probably bound to a specific site on the ribosome. Another inhibitor of protein synthesis, cycloheximide (Actidione), is not effective in bacteria but seems to function in mammals and fungi in a similar way as does

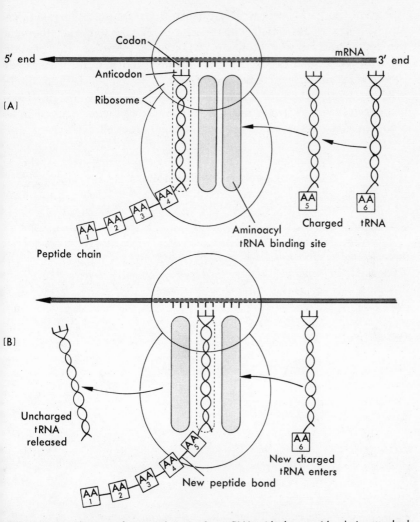

Codon

Anticodon

Ribosome

[A]

5′ end

mRNA

3′ end

Aminoacyl
tRNA binding site

Charged tRNA

Peptide chain

[B]

Uncharged
tRNA
released

New peptide bond

New charged
tRNA enters

Figure 2·10. The transfer reaction. In **A,** a tRNA with the peptide chain attached is shown. The new charged tRNA moves into position and is bound to the ribosome. The mRNA has already been bound to the small unit of the ribosome. Once the charged tRNA is in position, its amino acid is available for the formation of a new peptide bond. **B:** Uncharged tRNA is released and the growing peptide chain is then attached to the newly attached tRNA. At any time three tRNA molecules may be present on the ribosome: one that has just been released, one to which the peptide chain is attached, and one that has just been bound to the new amino acid.

Chloramphenicol. Normal release of the completed peptide chain occurs and the action of cycloheximide is easily reversible. Schweet suggested that cycloheximide acts on the enzyme system involved in the structural change of the ribosome.

POLYSOMES. Messenger RNA derived by transcription of DNA rapidly becomes associated with ribosomes. Presumably, the ribosome can only attach at the proper position for translation of a peptide from its N-terminal beginning end. In any case, as protein synthesis proceeds, a number of ribosomes become associated with a single mRNA; these structures are called *polysomes* (Figure 2·11). They have been observed by electron microscopy as well as recognized indirectly through density-gradient fractionation of the cell.

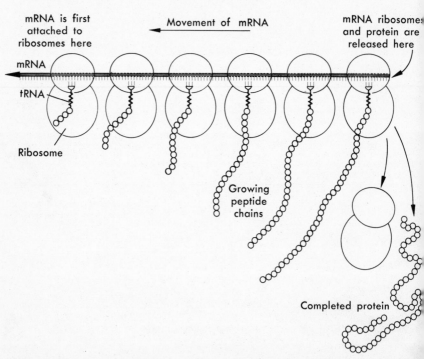

Figure 2·11. Diagrammatic representation of a polysome. A number of ribosomes are attached to mRNA. Each has progressed varying distances down the mRNA during translation. Each, therefore, has progressively longer protein chains attached. At the end of the message, the mRNA and ribosome separate and the complete protein is released.

Labeling techniques are used to identify mRNA as a component of polysomes. For example, a brief pulse label of ^{32}P or other radioactive precursors of RNA results in the association of the label with increasing numbers of ribosomes for a short period of time. Agents such as actinomycin D prevent RNA synthesis, thus reducing the number of polysome units produced.

Further indication that protein synthesis occurs on polysome structures has been obtained with amino acid incorporation experiments.

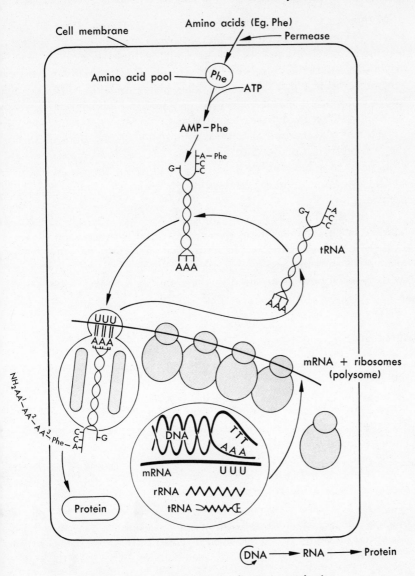

Figure 2·12. A cellular view of protein synthesis.

Following a brief pulse with radioactive amino acids, newly synthesized protein is found attached to polysomes. When a protein from such a pulse experiment is isolated, it has been shown that more label is associated with the C-terminal, the last end of the peptide to be synthesized. This suggests that peptides at various stages of completion are present in polysomes at all times. This further implies that read-off of the message proceeds sequentially down the message (from the 5' end of mRNA).

In the case of a polycistronic or multigenic message, it is not clear whether ribosomes can be attached at various places along the message or only at the beginning of the long chain. Furthermore, in higher organisms, ribosomes are attached to membranes—so it is probable that movement of mRNA occurs along ribosomes rather than the reverse. In any case, mRNA binds to the smaller 30-S subunit of ribosomes and tRNA binds to the larger 50-S subunit.

The fact that translation proceeds in a $5' \rightarrow 3'$ direction allows for the possibility of initiation of translation before transcription ($5' \rightarrow 3'$) of RNA is complete. This would further allow for the possibility that ribosomes play a regulatory role through initiation of the translation process.

Further mechanisms of chain initiation and termination will be discussed elsewhere, but all involve either special triplet codons (e.g., UAG) or rare tRNAs. Very recently, cytoplasmic factors have been recognized as being involved in chain initiation. A summary of the synthetic relationships involved in the transcription-translation process is presented in Figure 2·12.

The Genetic Code

Little in modern science matches the excitement of the cracking of the genetic code. The public followed the developments almost from the beginning, as the information appeared in *The New York Times* faster than it became available to the general scientific community. The drama was not lessened by the competition between the bright young scientist Marshall Nirenberg and the old pro Severo Ochoa, a Nobel prize laureate.

Given the basic DNA $\rightarrow$ RNA $\rightarrow$ protein relationship as the primary mode of information transfer in the cell, the problem of the genetic code can be clearly defined. The sequence relationships between the bases of the nucleic acid and the amino acids of the protein are important. Additional problems of code-word assignment and punctuation must be answered. Eventually the evolutionary logic of the system must be sought.

CELL-FREE SYSTEMS OF PROTEIN SYNTHESIS

In vitro, it is possible to carry out a limited and inefficient protein synthesis. Success requires a complicated combination of cell extracts. There is an absolute requirement for the three forms of RNA (messenger, transfer, and ribosomal), an energy source (ATP, GTP), and various enzyme fractions. In addition, radioactive amino acids are provided so that a very small amount of incorporation into protein can be detected. Radioactive amino acid incorporation is detected by precipitating the protein by means of acid and counting the radioactivity.

Primarily because of the extreme lability of mRNA coding for a complete protein, it has proved to be quite difficult to demonstrate the synthesis of a specific protein in a cell-free system (a notable exception has been the synthesis of hemoglobin by Schweet). However, it was this very difficulty that led Nirenberg and Matthaei to employ synthetic mRNA in place of natural mRNA in their amino acid incorporation experiments.

SYNTHETIC mRNA STUDIES. It was possible to prepare synthetic mRNA because of the availability of the enzyme polynucleotide phosphorylase, isolated by Ochoa and Grunberg-Manago. The enzyme catalyzes the conversion of ribonucleotide diphosphates to a polymer chemically similar to natural RNA. Different synthetic mRNA types could be made by altering the blend of the four ribonucleotide precursors of RNA. The nucleotide sequence of the product RNA was essentially random. For example, a polymer containing only adenine and uracil in equal proportions would be represented by all possible combinations of these bases in equal proportions. If the ratio of A/U was increased to 2:1 (from 1:1), the frequency by which A would appear in *any* particular triplet sequence would increase. (It is necessary that the coding unit contain at least three bases in order to have sufficient combinations to code for all twenty amino acids.)

Nirenberg and Matthaei first made use of a polymer of uracil alone (called *poly U*). They reasoned that if some sequence of U (triplet or otherwise) coded for a *particular* amino acid, it could be recognized in a cell-free incorporation experiment. Poly U was a good choice for other reasons: it binds well to ribosomes and, as it turned out, the product protein was insoluble and easy to isolate.

When poly U was presented as message to the cell-free system containing all amino acids, *one* was exclusively selected from the mixture. It was phenylalanine, so it could be concluded that some sequence of UUU coded for phenylalanine polymer. Other homopolymers (poly A, poly C, poly I) were inactive for phenylalanine incorporation.

Various blends of synthetic mRNAs were prepared and the calculated triplet frequency compared with the percentage of incorporation of a particular amino acid. Such an analysis allowed the assignment of tentative triplets to most of the amino acids—although in most cases the exact *order* of the three bases in the triplet was unknown. However, in spite of this and other problems, some tentative generalizations about the code could be drawn: (1) the code is degenerate, that is, a particular amino acid may be coded for by several codons; and (2) codons are ambiguous, that is, specificity of a codon for one amino acid is not absolute.

Degeneracy probably occurs because a variety of tRNA molecules with differing anticodon triplets are charged with the same amino acid (different words may mean the same amino acid). Ambiguity is probably due to different amino acids being attached to a particular tRNA with a single anticodon triplet (one word may mean different amino acids). Certain antibiotics also result in the attachment of the wrong amino acid to a particular tRNA.

TRINUCLEOTIDE BINDING STUDIES. Nirenberg also discovered that the addition of trinucleotides (three RNA bases) to a cell-free system causes the binding of a specific charged tRNA to the ribosomes. The various trinucleotides were prepared and binding experiments were carried out. Each trinucleotide was tested against all twenty different tRNAs, one of which was charged with a radioactive amino acid. Ribosomes can be separated from free tRNA by filtration on a mem-

TABLE 2·1

Codon Assignments from Polypeptide Synthesis or Stimulation of Aminoacyl-tRNA Binding to Ribosomes or Both

5'—OH TERMINAL BASE	MIDDLE BASE				3'—OH TERMINAL BASE
	U	C	A	G	
	Phe	Ser	Tyr	Cys	U
	Phe	Ser	Tyr	Cys	C
U	Leu	Ser	Nonsense		A
	Leu	Ser	Nonsense	Try	G
	Leu	Pro	His	Arg	U
	Leu	Pro	His	Arg	C
C	Leu	Pro	Gln	Arg	A
	Leu	Pro	Gln	Arg	G
	Ileu	Thr	Asn	Ser	U
	Ileu	Thr	Asn	Ser	C
A	Ileu	Thr	Lys	Arg	A
	Met	Thr	Lys	Arg	G
	Val	Ala	Asp	Gly	U
	Val	Ala	Asp	Gly	C
G	Val	Ala	Glu	Gly	A
	Val	Ala	Glu	Gly	G

brane filter so that the bound radioactivity can be counted and matched with the trinucleotide in question. For example, the trinucleotide $5'CAC3'$ promotes binding of histidine-charged tRNA to ribosomes.

Most of the sixty-four possible trinucleotides have been synthesized; Table 2·1 summarizes the combined coding data from polypeptide synthesis or tRNA binding experiments. It may be seen from the table that the code is highly degenerate. For a particular amino acid, the first two bases are often the same but the third (3′) base may be either purine or pyrimidine or any one of the four bases. In other cases, the first base may vary while the last two remain constant. Although the binding of the first tRNA appears to be nonenzymatic, it may develop that enzymes play a specifying role *in vivo*.

Sometimes metabolic or chemically related amino acids have similar codons. Jukes has suggested that there are fifteen doublet codes and, as new amino acids evolved, the third base did also—resulting in what we now see as a triplet code. Certainly more information is required than is present in a doublet code (sixteen combinations) to accommodate all twenty amino acids.

There are cases of codons (e.g., UAG) that do not appear to code for *any* amino acids. Such nonsense codons probably play a role in starting and stopping the reading of a genetic message (i.e., punctuation), which will be discussed later. One such system is known to function by causing the premature release of growing polypeptide chains.

References

Arnstein, H. R. V. "Mechanisms of Protein Synthesis," *Brit. Med. Bull.*, *21:* 217, 1965.

Bennett, T. P., and Earl Frieden. *Modern Topics in Biochemistry,* New York: Macmillan, 1966.

Brenner, S. "Collinearity and the Genetic Code," *Proc. Roy. Soc. (Ser. B)*, *164:* 170, 1966.

Crick, F. H. C. "On Protein Synthesis," *Symp. Soc. Exptl. Biol. 12:* 138, 1958.

Ingram, Vernon M. *The Biosynthesis of Macromolecules,* New York: W. A. Benjamin, Inc., 1965.

Lanni, Frank. "The Biological Coding Problem," *Adv. Genetics 12:* 1, 1964.

Nishimura, S., D. S. Jones, and H. G. Khorana. "Studies on Polynucleotides," *J. Mol. Biol. 13:* 302, 1965.

Schweet, Richard, and Roger Heintz. "Protein Synthesis," *Ann. Rev. Biochem. 35:* 727, 1966.

Singer, M. F., and P. Leder. "Messenger RNA: An Evolution," *Ann. Rev. Biochem. 35:* 195, 1966.

Stretton, A. O. W. "The Genetic Code," *Brit. Med. Bull. 21:* 229, 1965.

Taylor, J. Herbert (ed.). *Molecular Genetics,* part I, New York: Academic, 1963.

Taylor, J. Herbert (ed.). *Selected Papers on Molecular Genetics,* New York: Academic, 1965.

Watson, J. D. *Molecular Biology of the Gene,* New York: W. A. Benjamin, Inc., 1965.

Woese, C. R. "Order in the Genetic Code," *Proc. Nat. Acad. Sci. USA 54:* 71, 1965.

Vogel, H. J., V. Bryson, and J. Lampen (eds.). *Informational Macromolecules,* New York: Academic, 1963.

Gene-Enzyme Relationships: Genetic Control of Cellular Metabolism

THE PATHWAY and mode of information flow from the primary genetic molecule, DNA, through RNA and finally to protein structure has been described. This process has been of paramount interest to the molecular geneticist for the past ten years. However, the relationship between genes (DNA) and enzymes (proteins) was clear even before the structure of DNA was known. Studies by Beadle and Tatum in the early 1950s led to the formulation of the one-gene, one-enzyme hypothesis. This hypothesis firmly provided a biochemical basis for gene action, the effect of which was profound in the development of our current concepts of genetics.

Intermediary Metabolism and Biosynthetic Pathways

Many cells, especially microorganisms, have very simple nutritional requirements consisting of inorganic salts (minerals) and sugar. Thus these organisms are capable of converting a simple carbon source such as sucrose into all the essential cell constituents. This process is called *intermediary metabolism* and consists of stepwise chemical conversions within the cell.

Intermediary metabolism is organized into *biosynthetic pathways,* each leading to an essential product such as an amino acid or a vitamin. There is amazing similarity between biosynthetic pathways even in highly diverse organisms such as bacteria, plants, and man. A field of biochemistry has developed called *comparative biochemistry* that is concerned with similarities in intermediary metabolism in all organisms.

We might generalize a biosynthetic pathway leading from a precursor (e.g., a sugar) to a product (e.g., an amino acid) as a series of simple biochemical conversions involving several intermediates.

$$P \text{ (precursor)} \to A \to B \to C \to D \to E \text{ (end product)}$$

It is fairly easy to recognize the end product because it is an essential building block and can be found when we analyze the components of a cell. To describe all the intermediate steps leading from a sugar to an amino acid is far more difficult, however. Each step in intermediary metabolism is presumed to be under the control of an enzyme, which is a biological catalyst. If the cell is gently disrupted and carefully fractionated by centrifugation and precipitation techniques, a particular fraction will contain a protein capable of converting $D \to E$, for example. Such a study presents certain problems. First of all, we must have some of molecule D—this presumes we know the chemical nature of the intermediates. Second, the enzyme may be quite unstable and become inactive before we can isolate it. Finally, we must have an assay for the formation of the product of the enzymatic reaction.

Assuming all these difficulties have been met and solved, it turns out that each such step is mediated by a catalytic protein, the enzyme. One can generalize that precursors lead to products through stepwise biochemical conversions, each of which is catalyzed by separate enzymes. Such a generalization was the current state of knowledge when Beadle and Tatum began their studies. Relatively few of the intermediate steps had been assessed, but most of the end products were known. Enzymes were known to be proteins—markedly unstable and difficult to isolate without loss of activity.

BIOCHEMICAL MUTANTS

Beadle and Tatum selected the fungus *Neurospora crassa* for their studies. It has a simple nutritional requirement and exists in the haploid stage through most of its life cycle, although recombinational analysis can be carried out following a classical meiosis. Vegetative spores, or conidia, were used in treatments with mutagenic agents such as x-rays and ultraviolet light. Certain of the isolated mutants were unique in that they no longer were able to grow on a minimal medium but required complete media consisting of mixtures of cellular metabolites. Screening categories of the components of complete media —such as amino acids, vitamins, organic acids, purines, and pyrimidines—were devised. Particular mutants, when tested with these various supplements, were found to grow uniquely on certain subsets, such as amino acids. Further screening by growth assay on individual amino acids revealed a single requirement for a particular amino acid, for example, tryptophan (Figure 3·1). If this mutant (tryptophan-

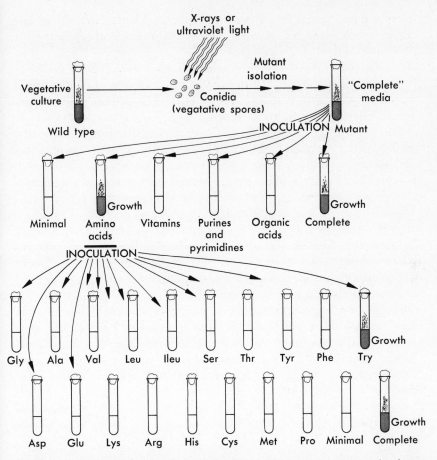

Figure 3·1. Screening of biochemical mutants of *Neurospora crassa*. A biochemical mutant will not grow on a minimal medium but will grow on complete media. Mixtures of amino acids, vitamins, etc. are tested first. In the example, growth only on amino acids is obtained. The amino acids are further tested to reveal a requirement for tryptophan.

less) strain is mated with a wild type, the tryptophanless condition can be shown to be inherited as a simple Mendelian gene that can be mapped at a particular genetic locus.

Through the years a wide variety of such mutants has been accumulated; they involve all the major biosynthetic pathways. As they were isolated it became clear that a collection of tryptophanless mutants, for example, represents several genetic loci that (in the case of *Neurospora*) map by recombination analysis on different chromosomes. These various mutants were presumed to correspond to the various steps leading to tryptophan (or any other end product for which a collection of mutants was available).

Several simple criteria could be applied to locate the site of the genetic block in the biosynthetic pathway. If, because of a mutation, a particular biosynthetic step could not be carried out, the block can be characterized in three ways: (1) material prior to the site of the block frequently accumulates; (2) any product past the site of the block will serve as a growth factor; and (3) no enzymatic activity can be demonstrated in the mutant for the blocked step.

In applying this analysis to the hypothetical biosynthetic pathway used earlier, we might expect the following type of observations (Figure 3·2). Mutant locus 1 accumulates compound C; both compounds D and E serve to satisfy the growth requirement of the mutant an enzyme 3 activity (catalyzing $C \rightarrow D$) is missing from its extracts. Mutant locus 4 might not only accumulate B and be missing enzyme 2 activity, but it may also grow on the material accumulated by mutant 1. Such cross-feeding relationships would position the two mutants relative to each other even though none of the intermediates had been chemically identified. Furthermore, the nature of many unidentified intermediates could be established because of the unique tendency for the substances to accumulate behind the biosynthetic block and therefore be available for isolation and characterization.

One of the first pathways to be studied leads to the amino acid arginine (Figure 3·3). As its intermediate steps have been elaborated over the years, arginine now affords an example of some of the complexities that tend to confuse such an analysis. One such complication is a branched pathway from a common precursor; another is a biosynthetic cycle. One can see in Figure 3·3 that glutamic acid is a com-

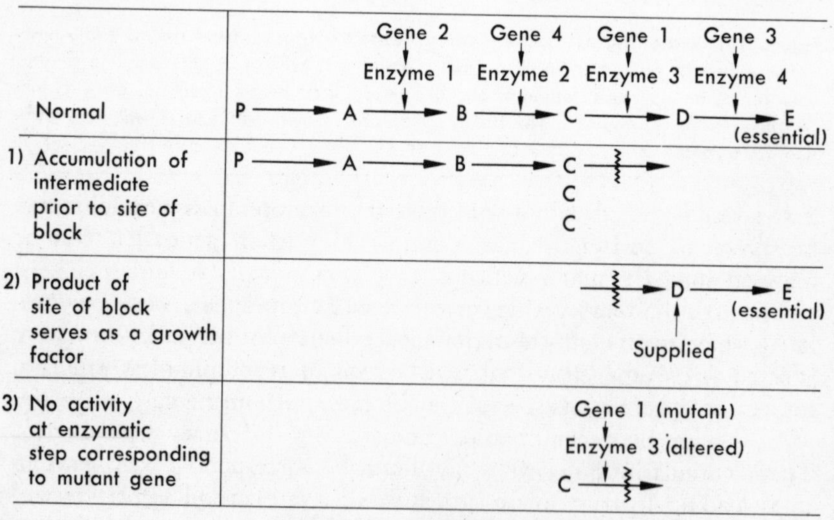

Figure 3·2. A genetic block.

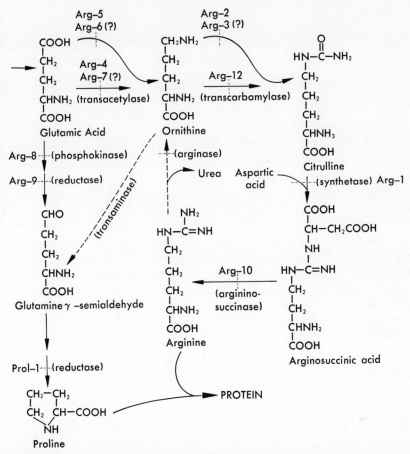

Figure 3·3. Arginine and proline biosynthesis. [After Fincham and Day, *Fungal Genetics*, 2nd ed., Philadelphia: F. A. Davis Company, 1963, p. 177.]

mon precursor of pathways leading to the amino acids proline and arginine. Both amino acids may be incorporated into protein, but part of the arginine molecule cycles back into its own pathway with the release of urea and ammonia.

The results of screening assays on various available intermediates are shown in Table 3·1. These intermediates may be related to the pathway for the biosynthesis of arginine and proline in *Neurospora* (Figure 3·3). One particular mutant class (arg-8) will grow on either arginine or proline, or on any of the intermediates except glutamic acid. This suggests that glutamic acid is the precursor of both the arginine and proline pathway. Furthermore, since proline will serve as a growth factor alone, it can be converted into arginine by the reverse of its normal pathway of biosynthesis.

TABLE 3·1
Screening-Assay Results

GENETIC LOCUS*	GLUTAMIC ACID	PROLINE	GLUTAMIC γ-SEMI-ALDEHYDE	ORNITHINE	CITRULLINE	ARGININE
I, Arg-1 / VII, Arg-10	−†	−	−	−	−	+
IV, Arg-2 / I, Arg-3	−	−	−	−	+	+
II, Arg-12 / V, Arg-4 / II, Arg-5	−	−	−	+	+	+
I, Arg-6 / V, Arg-7 / V, Arg-8 / ?, Arg-9	−	+	+	+	+	+
III, Prol-1	−	+	−	−	−	−

* The roman numerals refer to the chromosome on which the various genetic loci are located.
† The + and − signs indicate growth or lack of growth on minimal media supplemented with the designated intermediate.

INBORN ERRORS OF METABOLISM IN MAN

Garrod, an English physician, wrote a book in 1909 titled *Inborn Errors of Metabolism,* in which he discussed human genetic abnormalities that had their bases in modified body chemistry. Garrod's view that such conditions even *existed* was many years ahead of its time.

One particular disease he discussed was alcaptonuria, which we now know to involve degradation products of the amino acids phenylalanine and tyrosine. It is characterized by the accumulation of black pigment, a product of a material called homogentisic acid, in the urine of the individual. Homogentisic acid is normally converted (ultimately) to carbon dioxide and water. We now know this conversion to be catalyzed by an enzyme present in normal individuals and absent in those with alcaptonuria. Thus, this condition—known over fifty years ago—is actually a typical genetic block, with its corresponding missing enzyme.

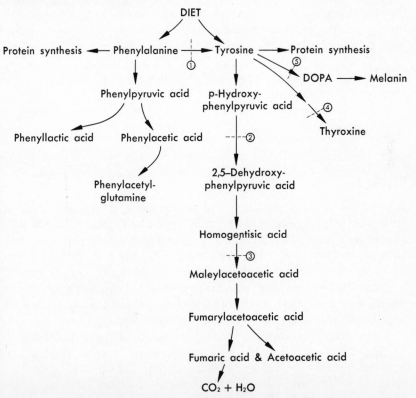

Figure 3·4. Phenylalanine and tyrosine metabolism in man. The sites of the genetic block in various inborn errors of metabolism are indicated: (1) phenylketonuria, (2) tyrosinosis, (3) alcaptonuria, (4) goiterous cretinism, and (5) albinism.

At least three other cases of similar metabolic blocks in phenylalanine-tryrosine metabolism of man are now known (Figure 3·4). One particularly interesting metabolic disease is *phenylketonuria.* It is far more serious than alcaptonuria because individuals with the disorder are mentally deficient. The biochemistry of the condition has been well described. Normally, phenylalanine is converted to tyrosine, which, if not used in building protein, is degraded (as mentioned above) to carbon dioxide and water. However, in the phenylketonuric individual there is no enzyme for the conversion of phenylalanine to tyrosine; thus the former accumulates in the body cells. Oxidation products of phenylalanine damage developing nervous tissue, resulting in the mental defect.

Still another condition is albinism, which is a well-known abnormality in man. In this case the pathway leading from tyrosine to melanin is blocked. Melanin is a basic building block of the pigments of man.

All the conditions shown in Figure 3·4 suggest the fundamental concept that genetic mutations result in the loss of the ability to carry out a particular enzymatically catalyzed biochemical reaction. In man, with his complex diet, the condition is not usually detected as a nutritional lesion but only when the block is manifested in other ways. Indeed, when human biochemistry is properly studied, it is clear that through the years man has lost the ability to carry out a number of metabolic reactions. He is, in a nutritional sense, one complex multiple biochemical mutant.

Gene Control of Protein (Enzyme) Structure

One of the really remarkable and intellectually satisfying studies in molecular genetics relates the enzyme tryptophan synthetase to a particular gene locus. The studies were started by the late David Bonner with *Neurospora* and have been extended with *E. coli* by Charles Yanofsky. The work of Yanofsky stands as a model of modern genetic research and a satisfying culmination of the early work begun by Beadle and Tatum. It represents the most complete study to date of both the fine structure of a gene and its corresponding enzyme.

Tryptophan synthetase, as the name suggests, controls the final step in the synthesis of the amino acid tryptophan. A number of steps are involved in the conversion of the aromatic amino acid precursor shikimic acid to anthranylic acid, through two more steps to indole glycerol phosphate (IGP) (Figure 3·5).

In the cell, indole glycerol phosphate is converted to tryptophan by means of the enzyme tryptophan synthetase (TSase). Two additional nonphysiological enzymatic conversions have proved useful for assay purposes. Bacterial TSase is composed of two nonidentical subunits called A protein and B protein. Mutants in the A gene result in the inability to grow unless indole or tryptophan is supplied. Mutants in the B gene are unable to grow on indole but still respond to tryptophan. Neither can carry out the physiological reaction IGP → Tryptophan but the above differences allow a distinction to be made between the two mutant types.

In summary, TSase is an enzyme complex with a molecular weight of 105,000; it can be dissociated into two subunits, the smaller (A) having a molecular weight of 29,500 and containing 272 amino acids.

Yanofsky isolated a large number of tryptophan-requiring mutants. They could be divided into two groups (A and B), depending on their growth response (as mentioned above). Genetically, the A mutants map in a cluster and the B mutants in an adjacent cluster. When the mutants were examined carefully it was found that most of them produce a protein that closely resembled normal TSase but had no (or little) enzymatic activity. Presumably such mutants would have very subtle though crucial changes in the enzyme structure. Yanofsky carried out his genetic and protein structure analysis with such a group of class-A mutants.

Ingram, in earlier work with hemoglobin, had developed an elegant technique for analysis of the fine structure of protein. The technique has been called *fingerprinting*. A pure protein is subjected to digestion by various proteolytic enzymes such as trypsin, chymotrypsin, or pepsin. Each enzyme has specificity for the type of peptide bond it attacks and cleaves. Trypsin, for example, breaks the bonds between the carboxyl group of lysine or arginine and the adjacent amino acid. Both the other enzymes cleave peptide bonds involving one of the aromatic amino acids—tryptophan, tyrosine, or phenylalanine. Digestion of a protein with such enzymes yields a number of smaller polypeptide subunits. The number and size depend on the number and kind of the above-mentioned peptide bridges that characterize the particular protein.

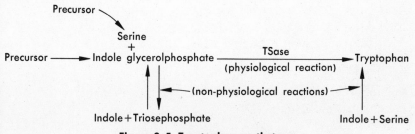

Figure 3·5. Tryptophan synthetase.

A fingerprint consists of a paper chromatogram in which the different peptides are separated to characteristic locations. These locations are highly reproducible and the various peptide subunits can be located and numbered. Digestion of a protein in which lysine, for example, has been replaced by another amino acid results in an altered fingerprint (misplaced peptide unit). Analysis of the amino acid content of this one peptide usually reveals which particular amino acid has replaced, in this case, lysine.

Yanofsky found that most of his mutants were altered by the simple substitution of one amino acid for another. Such a substitution results in the loss of functional activity of the gene product, the enzyme. Thus, *an altered gene yields an altered amino acid sequence in its corresponding enzyme.*

References

Bonner, David M. *Heredity,* Englewood Cliffs, N.J.: Prentice-Hall, 1961.

Fincham, J. R. S. *Microbial and Molecular Genetics,* London: The English University Press, Ltd., 1965.

Hartman, Philip E., and Sigmund R. Suskind. *Gene Action,* Englewood Cliffs, N.J.: Prentice-Hall, 1965.

Srb, A. M., R. D. Owen, and R. S. Edgar. *General Genetics,* San Francisco: Freeman, 1965.

Strauss, B. S. *An Outline of Chemical Genetics,* Philadelphia: Saunders, 1960.

Sutton, H. Eldon. *Genes, Enzymes and Inherited Diseases,* New York: Holt, 1961.

Wagner, R. P., and H. K. Mitchell. *Genetics and Metabolism,* 2nd ed. New York: Wiley, 1964.

Mutation: A Molecular View of the Process and Its Consequences

IF A TOUCHSTONE exists for genetics, it is mutation. The geneticist has always been dependent upon mutants, either natural or induced, for the study of the normal mechanism. Mendel worked with the variations found in natural population. Muller induced mutants in *Drosophila* by means of x-rays, which, along with other observations, resulted in a burst of scientific growth centering on that organism. Beadle and Tatum depended on mutants for their studies on gene-enzyme relationships. Benzer's studies on gene fine structure required not only mutants but specific types of mutants in large numbers. Reverse as well as suppressor mutations were demonstrated and both led to a better understanding of genetic coding. Currently the exciting phenomenon of genetic repair is under study—a process by which a cell can recognize and correct mutations within its own genetic material.

Early Mutational Studies

The early geneticist worked with mutations that were expressed as visible changes in the morphology of the organism, for example, eye color or wing structure in *Drosophila*. Such mutations were transmitted as changes in a single Mendelian gene. Most mutations were expressed as a recessive, or deficient, state that could be detected only in the diploid organism when present in combination with a similarly deficient allele. The fact that the normal gene was dominant over a mutant form of the same gene suggested that most mutations involved changes in the structure of a gene so that it no longer functioned normally.

H. J. Muller and others carried out systematic studies with ionizing radiations, such as x-rays, that produced chromosomal breaks. The frequency of such breaks was dependent on the dose of x-ray. He devised a technique for similarly studying lethal mutations on the X chromosome in *Drosophila*. Thus, x-ray caused both visible changes in chromosome structure and functional changes in a highly correlated manner.

Painter and Stone examined the giant salivary chromosomes of *Drosophila* and observed minute deficiencies, in particular, chromosomal bands associated with certain mutations. Genetic analysis correlated these deficiencies with the map position of the mutant gene on the chromosome. Thus, as early as the 1930s, it was possible to relate a gene that occupied a particular position on the chromosome to an altered hereditary expression such as eye color in *Drosophila* (Figure 4·1).

Shortly thereafter it was demonstrated that ultraviolet light would cause mutations—probably because of the selective absorption of ultraviolet light by nucleic acids. This suggested that mutation resulted from changes not only in chromosomes but specifically in the DNA present in the chromosomes.

Beadle and Tatum employed both ionizing and ultraviolet radiation to induce biochemical mutants. Thus, a mutational expression was extended from the morphological to the physiological level through correlating mutation and loss of enzymatic capability to carry out a particular biochemical reaction in the cell. As discussed elsewhere, an extension of these mutational studies has been more than fruitful.

Through all these years a discussion continued as to what constituted a mutation as far as the gene structure was concerned. It was possible that ionizing radiation actually deleted the gene by causing

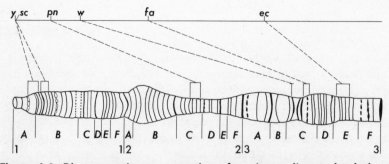

Figure 4·1. Diagrammatic representation of a giant salivary gland chromosome of *Drosophila*. Changes in the bands may be correlated with the indicated mutations: *y*, yellow body; *sc*, scute bristles; *pn*, prune; *w*, white eyes; *fa*, facet eyes; *ec*, echinus. [From C. B. Bridges, in *J. Hered.*, 26: 60, 1935.]

two breaks in the chromosome, with subsequent rejoining of the broken chromosome and loss of a segment. However, no such changes could be observed in certain cases, and a number of prominent geneticists suggested that the changes were minute and internal to the gene's structure. These minute changes were called *point mutations*. Only a few geneticists who possessed better knowledge of the molecular basis of heredity suggested that modification of the chemical structure of the genetic material might be expressed as a mutation. These discussions took on more meaning after Giles demonstrated that reversion of biochemical mutations could be induced with a variety of mutagens. Mutants that were characteristically unable to grow in the absence of a particular amino acid, for example, could be "back mutated" to the wild-type nutritional condition without an amino acid requirement. Indeed a mutation could be carried back and forth any number of times—a phenomenon suggesting a typical chemical reverse reaction.

The Molecular Basis of Mutation

The Watson-Crick model for DNA has been fundamental in the development of mutagenesis theories. Mechanisms of mutagenesis include: (1) modification of the structure of DNA or a component base of DNA; (2) substitution of one base for a different base; (3) deletion or addition of one base in one DNA strand; (4) deletion or addition of one or more base pairs in both strands of DNA; and (5) inversion of a sequence of nucleotide base pairs within the DNA molecule. All such changes result in different informational content of DNA, which is transmitted through replication to cell progeny or by transcription to mRNA.

TRANSITIONS AND TRANSVERSIONS

Freese has classified changes that ultimately result in single base substitutions as *transitions* or *transversions*. Replication of DNA may be required before a transition can occur, or a direct modification of the structure of one base may effectively substitute one base for another. In any case, the final effect is the replacement of a G≡C pair by an A=T pair (or the reverse). The purine-pyrimidine orientation is preserved. Transversions would result in a new orientation of the purine-pyrimidine relationship such as might occur when G≡C is replaced by C≡G. Both processes are summarized in Figure 4·2.

Nitrous acid (HONO) has been long known as a mutagenic chemical, but it was first thought to affect protein structure exclusively. It is, however, a highly effective agent for the oxidative deamination of

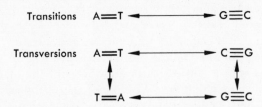

Transitions   A═T ◄────────► G≡C

Transversions   A═T ◄────────► C≡G

T═A ◄────────► G≡C

Figure 4·2. Mutation by transition and transversion of bases of DNA. Transitions involve the conversion of one purine base to another purine (or a pyrimidine to a pyrimidine). During replication, the second (different) purine, having altered base-pairing properties, guides an incorrect base into position. Thus, one normal base pair is converted to another pair that is genetically incorrect. Transversions involve the substitution of a purine by a pyrimidine (or vice versa). The substituted pyrimidine would, of course, normally pair with a purine—resulting in a molecule with a pyrimidine-purine base where there had been a purine-pyrimidine base pair. The left-right orientation of bases in the DNA molecule is preserved in the above illustration.

nucleic acid bases that contain free amino groups. Thus, deamination of adenine produces hypoxanthine, cytosine deaminates to uracil, and guanine deaminates to xanthine (Figure 4·3). In each case the deamination process results in the transition of an amino base to a keto base. It should be recalled that the base pairing in DNA involves ketoamino relationships through shared hydrogen bonding.

From Figure 4·3, it is evident that hypoxanthine (formerly adenine) will pair as though it were guanine, that is, with cytosine resulting in a transition of A═T to G═C. A similar transition occurs involving uracil (formerly cytosine) converting G═C to A═T. As the deamination product of guanine still resembles guanine, no mutation is likely to occur (Figure 4·4).

One would predict that nitrous acid would produce both forward and backward mutations; this has been supported in certain studies. However, exceptions exist. One type involves what is called a *second site suppressor*, which results in a compensating change at another base site. (This will be discussed later.)

A number of agents other than nitrous acid (e.g., hydroxylamine)

Figure 4·3. Base pairing and replication of deaminated bases. Adenine is deaminated to hypoxanthine, which is more like guanine and thus pairs with cytosine (AT → GC). Cytosine is deaminated to uracil, which pairs with adenine during replication (GC → AT). Guanine is deaminated to xanthine, which still resembles guanine and therefore pairs correctly with cytosine. In each case an amino base is converted to a keto base. Since base pairing in DNA involves ketoamino H-bonding relationships, the normal pairing specificity is altered.

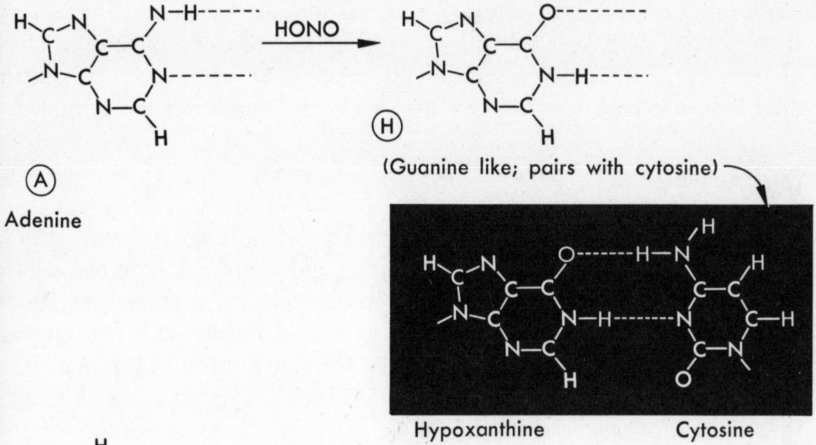

(A) Adenine

$\xrightarrow{\text{HONO}}$

(H)

(Guanine like; pairs with cytosine)

Hypoxanthine   Cytosine

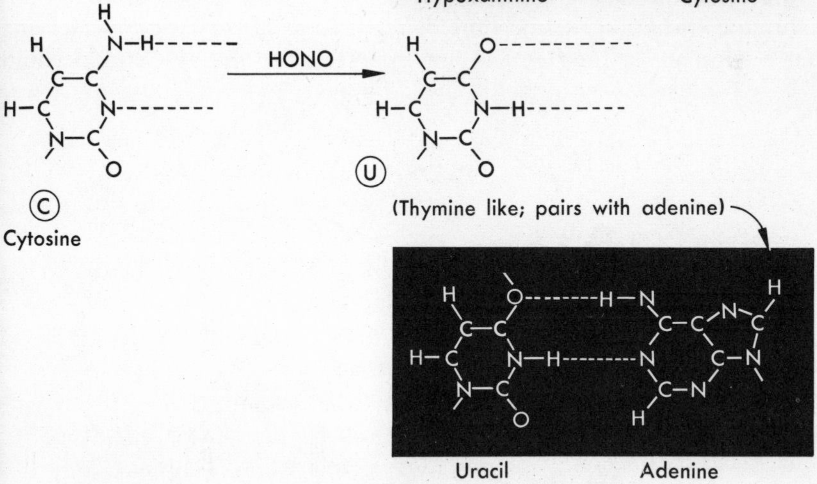

(C) Cytosine

$\xrightarrow{\text{HONO}}$

(U)

(Thymine like; pairs with adenine)

Uracil   Adenine

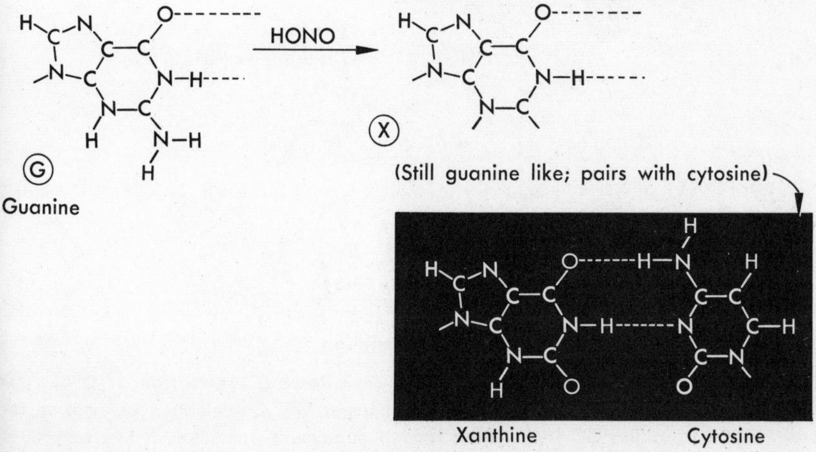

(G) Guanine

$\xrightarrow{\text{HONO}}$

(X)

(Still guanine like; pairs with cytosine)

Xanthine   Cytosine

results in the chemical alteration of resting nucleic acid. Certain of these agents, such as ethylmethane sulfonate, lead to depurination (loss of purines). Other alkylating agents, such as the nitrogen and sulfur mustards, are highly mutagenic but less well defined in their action.

TAUTOMERISM

Each of the four natural bases in DNA can exist in rare states, because of redistribution of the electrons and protons in the molecule; these changes are called tautomeric shifts. Certain of these rare states are such that the base cannot form hydrogen bonds with its complementary base but, in some cases, may form hydrogen bonds with the wrong base (Figure 4·5). Watson and Crick suggested some time ago that such tautomeric shifts might account for spontaneous mutations through transitions at the time of replication. Either the base serving as a template or the free base incorporated into the new strand could

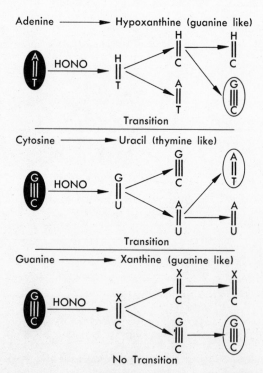

Figure 4·4. Consequences of base changes following replication of DNA. Deamination of adenine results in the transition AT → GC. Deamination of cytosine results in the transition GC → AT. Even though guanine is deaminated, two bonds remain for normal hydrogen bonding with cytosine so that no mutation is induced.

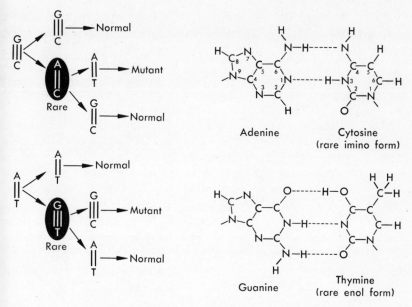

Figure 4·5. Tautomeric shifts involving cytosine and thymine. Cytosine would normally hydrogen bond with guanine and thymine with adenine. In their *rare* states (indicated above) they pair incorrectly—resulting in a transition in both cases illustrated.

exist in its rare state at the time of base pairing at the growing end of the chain. The result would be a DNA molecule with a forbidden base pair. Such a pair would be analogous to the nitrous acid–induced transition in that, at replication, one purine (or pyrimidine) would be substituted for the other.

It has been calculated that tautomeric shifts occur with a frequency too high to account for the extremely low frequency of spontaneous mutations (assuming most can be detected). Koch has suggested that the replicative enzymes are capable of discrimination and rejection of certain rare states. This, of course, suggests that the enzyme itself determines which base pairings are permissible and that such pairings would not depend solely on hydrogen bonding during replication. Similar forms of enzymatic proofreading will be discussed later.

BASE ANALOGUES

Certain analogues of the naturally occurring bases have been shown to be highly effective mutagenic agents. The natural base thymine (T), which is 5-methyluracil, has as its structural analogue 5-bromouracil (5-BU). It might be that if 5-BU is so similar to T, it could safely substitute for thymine and normal replication could occur.

However, its properties are such that one of the nitrogens involved in hydrogen bonding (N 1) is more frequently ionized than is the same nitrogen in thymine. In addition, 5-BU would be expected to undergo tautomeric shifts more frequently. In either case, a loss of one hydrogen occurs and this hydrogen is normally involved in hydrogen bonding (Figure 4·6).

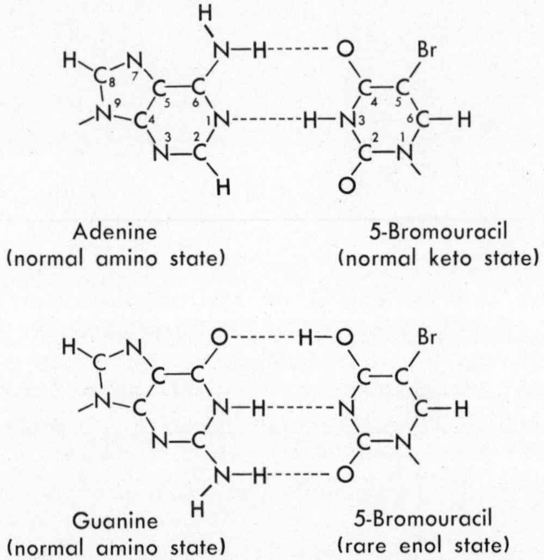

Adenine   5-Bromouracil
(normal amino state)   (normal keto state)

Guanine   5-Bromouracil
(normal amino state)   (rare enol state)

Figure 4·6. Base pairing of 5-bromouracil, a structural analogue of thymine. Normally 5-bromouracil (5-BU) will pair with adenine. However, a rare state occurs that allows hydrogen bonding with guanine. This may—depending on when the rare state occurs—result in two alternative types of mutagenic events.

Again, base-pair transitions would be predicted because of the pairing of 5-BU with guanine instead of with the correct base, adenine. This pairing mistake could occur either when BU enters DNA—a mistake in incorporation—or after it has been incorporated and undergone a new replication—a mistake in replication (Figure 4·7). The role of discrimination that enzymes of replication play would apply to the ionized 5-BU just as to the rare tautomeric states discussed above. The observation that the amount of 5-BU incorporated is not proportional to the frequency of mutation lends support to the hypothesis.

Another mutagenic base analogue is 2-amino purine (2-AP), but it exercises its action by a very different mechanism. Although it is occasionally incorporated for adenine, which it resembles, it will pair in its normal tautomeric state with both pyrimidine bases: thymine, which is correct, and cytosine, which is incorrect (Figure 4·8). In the

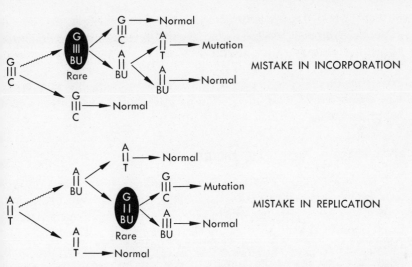

Figure 4·7. Base-pair transitions by 5-bromouracil. A mistake in incorporation occurs when the rare enol state of 5-BU occurs as it is incorporated into DNA. It thus acts not like thymine but like cytosine. Alternatively, 5-BU may be incorporated into DNA (as thymine) but undergo a shift to the rare enol state so that during replication abnormal pairing to 5-BU occurs. One type of mistake results in a G-C → A-T transition and the other in an A-T → G-C transition.

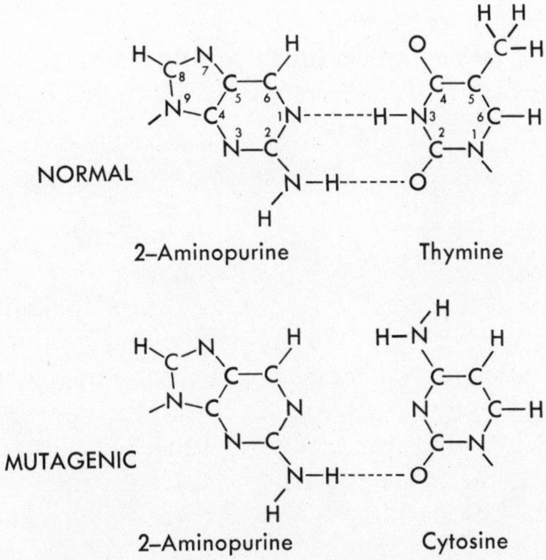

Figure 4·8. Base pairing of 2-aminopurine (2-AP). During replication, 2-AP normally would be incorporated in place of adenine (paired with T), which would not be mutagenic. However, during replication, the normal tautomeric state of 2-AP will allow pairing with cytosine, which would be mutagenic. Such pairing may also occur during replication so base-pair transitions can occur in both directions. Pairing of 2-AP with C can also occur (with two H bonds) in its rare tautomeric state.

former case (T), two hydrogen bonds are involved; with cytosine only one hydrogen bond is involved—the latter mutagenic condition occurring less frequently. In addition, one of the tautomeric states of 2-AP will pair with cytosine through two hydrogen bonds. Even an extremely small amount of 2-AP incorporation is highly mutagenic. Base-pair transitions are induced in both directions, and the analogue has proved to be a particularly useful mutagen.

SINGLE BASE DELETIONS AND ADDITIONS

Various alkylating agents, such as the sulfur and nitrogen mustards and the less toxic ethyl methanesulfonate (EMS), are effective mutagens. They react primarily on the base guanine, resulting in a labile deoxyriboside linkage so that an alkyl guanine is released from the DNA. This does not disturb the DNA backbone; thus the base can be replaced by any of the four bases, resulting in either transitions or transversions. (The evidence for transversions is, however, meager.)

Another mutagen, acridine, is believed to function by causing the addition or deletion of bases. The best evidence suggests intercalation of the acridine molecule between two otherwise sequential bases (Figure 4·9). The inserted base results in a limited untwisting and extension of the double-helix. This results in the distance between neighboring bases being extended from 6 to 8 Å, or double the distance as found in normal DNA. If acridine is present in the template strand, an extra base may be added during replication. On the other

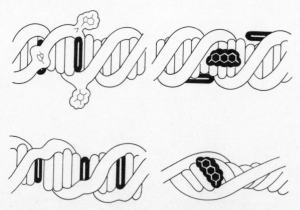

Figure 4·9. Possible structures of the intercalation complex of DNA with acridines. Acridine is inserted between adjacent bases, forcing them apart. If this occurs in the template strand, an extra base may be inserted in the new strand. If it is present during replication, it may temporarily insert for a base and then be released —resulted in a gap or deleted base in the replicating strand. [from fig. 2, L. S. Lerman, J. Cell. & Comp. Physiol., 64:2.]

hand, if it is present during replication, it may insert in the new strand
—thus masking the opposing base on the template strand. The new
strand will replicate with the deleted base, thus shortening the DNA
molecule by one base.

FRAME-SHIFT MUTANTS

Crick and his coworkers, in an analysis of acridine-induced mutants,
provided an elegant hypothesis to explain certain types of suppressor
mutations as well as the transcription process. Suppressor mutations
are mutants that revert the phenotype to normal by means of a second
mutation at a different site. Suppressors may be located at any point
in the genome, but those in question belong to a special class called
intragenic suppressors. Yanofsky has more properly called such specific

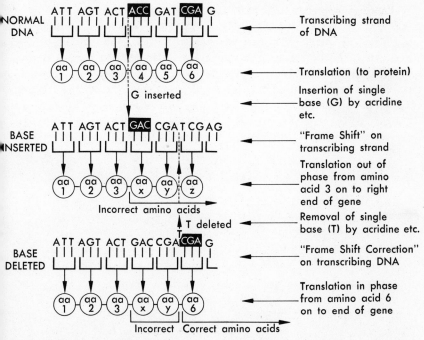

Figure 4·10. Frame-shift mutations. The transcribing strand of DNA that is shown
codes for RNA, which in turn is translated into amino acid sequence in protein. If
base would result in a complete change in the sequence of amino acids until the end
bases are read in frames of three from the left end of the gene, the insertion of one
of the gene was reached. However, if a second base were removed, the frame would
again be reset and the message would be in phase again. The protein might function
if the incorrect amino acid run were not in a crucial region.

types of mutants *second-site suppressors;* he showed that they occur within the structure of the gene itself.

A particular acridine-induced mutant might, for the sake of argument, have been produced by the deletion of a base. One would expect that a revertant of this particular mutant might have required reinsertion of the base. However, genetic analysis of acridine-induced revertants shows that a second mutation occurred at a nearby site; hence, acridine-induced reversions are not true reversions but are caused by second-site suppression.

Crick reasoned that some particular base in DNA constituted the initiation point for transcription of RNA and that the transcription proceeded in one direction from that point. If reading occurred triplet by triplet, deletion of a single base would render the remainder of the gene read-off gibberish. This is true if bases were read *always* in sets of three. The deletion of one would shift the reading frame one base to the left and thus completely change the code sense of the remaining DNA in that sequence. If each triplet codes a single amino acid (as it appears), that peptide up to the deletion would be correct but would be nonsense from that point on. Reinsertion of a new base (any base) nearby would reset the frame again and the remainder of the mRNA and protein formed would be normal (Figure 4·10). If that portion of the protein coded by the bases between the two sites was not essential to the enzyme function, the effect would be a reversion. The enzyme, although functionally normal (or near normal) would, of course, contain an altered amino acid sequence corresponding to the nonsense sequence in the suppressed mutant's DNA.

MUTATION AS REFLECTED IN PROTEIN STRUCTURE

It is perhaps surprising that the first example of a mutant expression in a protein molecule occurred in man. A number of mutations that affect hemoglobin function are transmitted in a Mendelian fashion and as a single gene. The most definitive study of this system was carried out by Ingram in a detailed analysis of the amino acid sequences in the hemoglobin molecule.

Adult wild-type hemoglobins consist of two pairs of peptide chains called α and β in Hemoglobin A. Thus, the molecule is a tetramer consisting of two α chains and two β chains $(\alpha\alpha\beta\beta)$, as shown in Figure 4·11. Each chain is controlled by separate structural genes, the α gene and the β gene. Mutations are known that affect either gene; one mutation has long been recognized as the cause of sickle-cell anemia. The condition is characterized by the formation of aggregates within the red blood cell resulting in a peculiar and distorted cell shape—the sickle cell. These cells are often destroyed, resulting in severe hemolytic anemia. In 1949 Pauling showed that patients with the

Figure 4·11. Hemoglobin molecule as deduced from x-ray diffraction studies. The hemoglobin molecule consists of two identical α chains (light blocks) and two identical β chains (dark blocks). Each chain is under the control of two separate structural genes. [From Bennett and Frieden, 1966.]

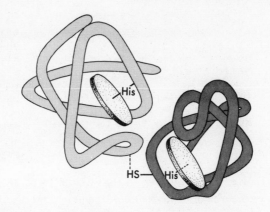

disease have a hemoglobin that can be distinguished from the normal on the basis of slower movement in an electrophoretic field (Figure 4·12). This suggested a change difference in the molecule and was referred to as a molecular disease.

The hemoglobin S (mutant) was shown to differ from hemoglobin A (normal) by the substitution of valine for glutamic acid as the sixth amino acid from the end of the β chain. Each chain has approximately 140 amino acids, and has a molecular weight of about 16,000. This means that the molecular disease is due to a single incorrect amino acid in a single protein molecule among the thousands of such molecules making up the cell. This observation with naturally occurring mutants gave support to the Beadle-Tatum hypothesis, which relates genes to protein structure, and offered direct evidence that a mutation in a gene results in a change in the template for hemoglobin.

Other mutant forms of hemoglobin were studied; they were all characterized by a single amino acid replacement at a unique site along the polypeptide chain. Such substitutions are summarized in Figure 4·13.

The work of Yanofsky has demonstrated similar relationships between mutations and changes in a particular protein. In this case, the protein was the enzyme tryptophan synthetase (TSase). Again, changes involving substitutions of one amino acid for another were

Figure 4·12. Electrophoretic mobility of hemoglobin molecules. Such mobility patterns provided early evidence of sickle-cell anemia, a molecular disease.

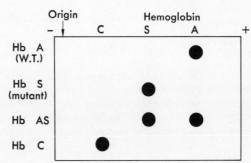

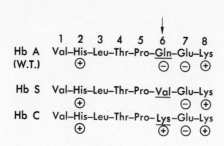

Figure 4·13. Amino acid sequences in the β chain of hemoglobin. Amino acid number 6 from the N-terminal valine end of the β chain has been substituted by valine in Hb S and by lysine in Hb C. Other amino acid substitutions occur at other sites in other hemoglobin varients. Similar mutational effects have also been observed in the α chain.

observed. However, in the case of TSase in *E. coli,* it was also possible to carry out fine-structure genetic analysis and to pinpoint the relative location of mutations within the gene structure itself (see Chapter 7). It was found that there is colinearity of the gene with its product, the polypeptide chain (Figure 4·14). Yanofsky has further demonstrated different mutations within the same triplet coding unit and has been able to achieve recombination between the subunits bases of the codon.

Tobacco mosaic virus is unusual in that its genetic material is RNA rather than DNA. Mutations—particularly with chemical mutagens such as nitrous acid—can, however, be induced in RNA. Certain such mutations are reflected as amino acid substitutions in the coat protein of the virus, which consists of many identical subunits (each contain-

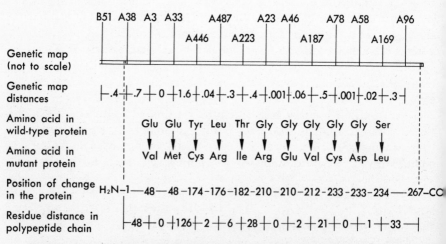

Figure 4·14. Colinear relationship between the genetic map and amino acid sequence of the A protein (α) of tryptophan synthetase. The relative positions of mutations are reflected as identical relative positions of amino acid substitutions in tryptophan synthetase, for which the exact sequences of all 267 amino acids are known. [From Yanofsky *et al., Proc. Nat. Acad. Sci.* 57: 298, 1967.]

ing 158 amino acids). These amino acid substitutions are scattered throughout the peptide chain.

A further correlation exists between the amino acid substitutions and the predicted allowable changes as based on current knowledge of the genetic code (see Chapter 2). These data suggest that in TMV the genetic RNA acts as messenger in protein synthesis because the mutants are those that would be expected for template rather than complementary nucleotide sequence.

Genetic Repair Mechanisms

EXCISION OF ULTRAVIOLET PHOTOPRODUCTS

Ultraviolet (UV) light, particularly of wavelengths absorbed by DNA, is highly effective both as a mutagen and in killing bacteria. The first photochemical lesion found in DNA was the formation of thymine dimers. This usually involves linkage, through covalent bonds, of adjacent thymine bases in the same strand of DNA. Such thymine dimers (T T) block DNA replication and are responsible for at least a large part of the adverse biological effects. When UV-irradiated bacterial cells are treated with visible light, thymine dimers are eliminated. This process involves a light-dependent photoreactivating enzyme and is called *photoreactivation*.

The most exciting of these studies are those that involve a dark repair of UV damage. Again, thymine dimers are lost; however, the loss is due to an excision process by which they are removed from the DNA molecule. These excised thymine dimers may be recovered in association with several adjoining bases in the soluble cellular fraction. Thus it appears that a section of one of the DNA strands near the thymine dimer is removed enzymatically during the dark-repair process. It is obvious that excision is only the first step in dark repair. Another step involves the replacement of the excised section of DNA. Presumably the genetic information for synthesis of the gap comes from the opposite complementary strand of DNA. Finally, the broken phosphodiester backbone is rejoined. Such a process has been called by Setlow the cut-and-patch mechanism (Figure 4·15).

Certain mutants of *E. coli* are characterized by the fact that they are UV-sensitive. In these mutants, the previously described excision does not occur. The question arises as to whether mutations are repaired or whether repair results only in resumption of DNA synthesis, thus preventing cell death. Witkin has shown that at least 99 percent of the mutants observed in a sensitive strain are prevented from developing in a resistant strain by repair that includes excision.

It has been observed that T_1 or λ bacteriophage treated with UV

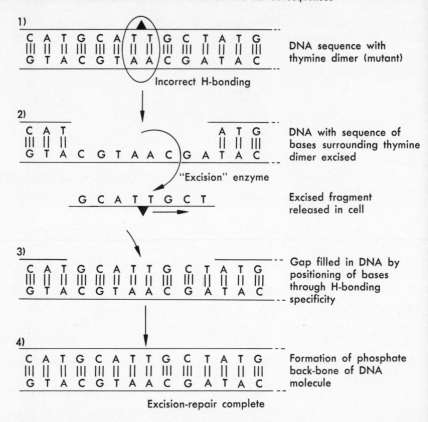

Figure 4·15. Hypothetical excision-repair mechanisms for mutational damage. Ultraviolet light results in the formation of thymine-thymine dimers. These are excised by means of a repair enzyme. The gap is then filled with normal bases which hydrogen bond to the unaltered half-helix of DNA. The phosphate backbone is completed and the original double-helix structure is restored.

light have higher infectivity when plated on resistant (wild-type) cells than when plated on radiosensitive mutants. This fact suggests that the irradiated phage DNA is repaired in resistant cells but not in the UV-sensitive mutants. A large number of UV-sensitive (phage-resistant) mutants have been isolated and have been found to represent three genetic loci that have been mapped. All three loci control the excision of thymine dimers from DNA. At the present time, the function of the product of the three genes is unknown. Presumably all three loci function jointly in the repair process.

Limited studies have been carried out on repair of lesions caused by agents other than ultraviolet light. X-ray damage is repaired to a limited extent and survival due to nitrous acid treatment is higher in resistant strains. Thus it might be generalized that repair enzymes recognize base-pairing errors that are excised by the enzymatic repair system under genetic control. Such discoveries are indeed exciting.

DNA REPAIR AND GENETIC RECOMBINATION

It is a logical postulate that if enzymes are involved in recombination for purposes of rejoining the phosphate backbone of DNA, those same enzymes might be involved in the same step during repair processes. Mutants of *E. coli* have been isolated that have lost the capacity to form recombinants when mated with suitable donor strains. In such mutants the lesion appears to be at the level of integration of DNA into the recipient chromosome because they accept the genetic material normally.

When recombination-deficient (Rec^-) mutants were examined for sensitivity to UV irradiation, they were found to be quite sensitive and capable of degrading their own DNA following irradiation. Additional x-ray–sensitive mutants were also found to be recombination-defective. The mechanism of action of the genes that affect recombination is not known at present.

MUTATOR GENES

Certain genes are known in a variety of organisms that increase the mutation rate of other genes. Yanofsky suggested several possible mechanisms for mutator-gene action: (1) a polymerase that makes errors during replication; (2) the production of mutagenic base analogues that lead to replication or incorporation errors; or (3) modification of DNA bases leading to replication errors.

Indeed two of these postulated mechanisms have been verified experimentally. Speyer discovered a mutant gene that produces an abnormal polymerase that results in a mutator effect on other genes. This observation suggests that there is much we do not know about replication mechanisms. Such an instance represents a case in which an enzyme, rather than hydrogen bonding alone, appears to determine which base is inserted—the latter process suggested from the Watson-Crick model for replication.

Yanofsky has observed that the *E. coli* mutator gene is specific and appears to act by altering bases present in DNA. The GC content of the organism is changed, which presumably results in a similar change in the amino acid content of proteins.

References

Freese, Ernst. "Molecular Mechanisms of Mutations," in J. Herbert Taylor (ed.), *Molecular Genetics,* New York: Academic, 1963, part I, p. 207.

Kreig, David R. "Specificity of Chemical Mutagenesis," in J. N. Davidson and W. E. Cohn (eds.), *Progress in Nucleic Acid Research,* New York: Academic, 1963, vol. 2, pp. 125–168.

Lawley, P. D. "Effect of Some Chemical Mutagens and Carcinogens on Nucleic Acids," in J. N. Davidson and W. E. Cohn (eds.), *Progress in Nucleic Acid Research,* New York: Academic, 1966, vol. 5, pp. 89–131.

Wacker, A. "Molecular Mechanisms of Radiation Effects," in J. N. Davidson and W. E. Cohn (eds.), *Progress in Nucleic Acid Research,* New York: Academic, 1963, vol. 1, pp. 369–399.

Witken, E. "Radiation Induced Mutations and Their Repair," *Science 152:* 1345, 1966.

Yanofsky, Charles. "Gene-Enzyme Relationships," in I. C. Gunsalus and R. Y. Stainer (eds.), *The Bacteria,* New York: Academic, 1964, vol. 5, p. 373.

Genetic Regulation: Cellular Control Systems

It is almost implicit that genetic regulation occurs in view of the fact that a fundamental characteristic of living organisms is their highly ordered activity. Investigation of the complex regulatory mechanisms that operate in higher organisms such as man have been broached only in recent studies involving hormone action and the molecular basis of memory. However, the intricacies of cellular regulatory mechanisms have yielded to experimental study with microorganisms. We can now describe in some detail the genetic mechanisms of regulation at the molecular level, as such mechanisms occur in single cells. (It is hoped that such studies can be successfully extended to more complex systems within the next few years.)

The simplest pattern of control of cellular activity is that which involves a sequence of enzymatic steps. Evidence has been presented relating genes to enzymes and, as might be expected, the mode of control is at this level. One mechanism involves control of enzymatic *activity* and another the control of enzymatic *synthesis*. In the latter case, the direct involvement of special genes called *regulatory genes* produces products that in turn respond to the chemical environment of the cell.

Regulation of Enzyme Activity

Certain studies in the late 1950s were concerned with a phenomenon that has come to be known as end product or *feedback inhibition*. (Figure 5·1). When the end product of a biosynthetic pathway is added to a culture of bacteria, the enzymatic activity of some earlier step is frequently inhibited. The effect is immediate and results in no

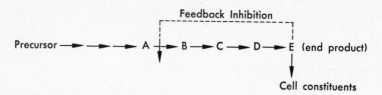

Figure 5·1. Feedback inhibition. When the end product (E) builds up to a particular concentration in the cell, it combines with an enzyme catalyzing an earlier step in the biosynthetic pathway (A → B). This results in no further synthesis of end product E from precursor A. Once the end product is depleted, the enzyme is released and synthesis is resumed.

further synthesis of the end product as long as that product persists in high concentrations in the cell.

Umbarger demonstrated the phenomenon in *E. coli,* and the pathway he studied involved the biosynthesis of the amino acid isoleucine. Threonine is an early precursor of isoleucine and the conversion to isoleucine requires five enzymatic steps (Figure 5·2). If isoleucine is added to the growth medium, further isoleucine synthesis is quenched and the added (exogenous) isoleucine is preferentially used. When the enzymes are extracted, it can be demonstrated that the enzyme catalyzing the conversion of threonine to a-ketobutyrate is inhibited in vitro. The effect in the cell is that of preventing further synthesis of isoleucine (as well as all the intermediates); this condition is maintained until the isoleucine supply is depleted.

Thus, feedback inhibition is characterized by its action on *preformed* enzymes; it does not affect synthesis. A single enzyme—usually the first one in the biosynthetic pathway—is affected, and the effect is immediate. The process is highly specific, as demonstrated in cases involving a branched pathway (Figure 5·2). Two enzymes may catalyze the conversion of a single precursor to two different products. These enzymes, specific for a single substrate, differ in that they are sensitive only to their respective end product.

The interaction between the enzyme and inhibitor is unique because the inhibitor is structurally quite different from the normal substrate. The normal substrate and the inhibitor (end product) do not compete for the same binding site on the enzyme. It is as though the enzyme has two sites, one specific for the substrate and one specific for the inhibitor (Figure 5·3). Binding of the inhibitor results in a change at the catalytic site. This phenomenon has been called an *allosteric transition* by Monod and Jacob. Such transitions frequently involve changes in bonding between protein subunits, thus altering the catalytic properties of the enzyme. In recent years, the term *allosteric interaction* has been broadened to include any change in the activity of an enzyme that is brought about by the selective binding at a second site on the enzyme not overlapping the substrate binding site. In effect, the enzyme becomes a chemical transducer that allows the interaction between two molecules (inhibitor and substrate) that might not otherwise interact.

As might be expected, mutants are known to occur that affect one site without affecting the other. Such mutants are resistant to feedback inhibition and produce large amounts of the end product. Certain such mutants can be isolated as clones resistant to amino acid

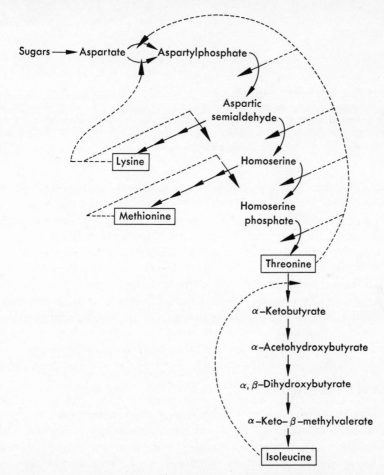

Figure 5·2. End product (feedback) inhibition of the aspartate family of amino acids. Aspartate gives rise to the amino acids lysine, methionine, threonine, and isoleucine. The dotted lines indicate interactions between particular end-product amino acids and enzymes involved in their biosynthesis. The specificity of the system is illustrated, for example, by the conversions of homoserine to either threonine or methionine. Methionine acts as an inhibitor of the homoserine enzyme in the methionine pathway only. Threonine similarly affects the conversion of homoserine, but only to threonine.

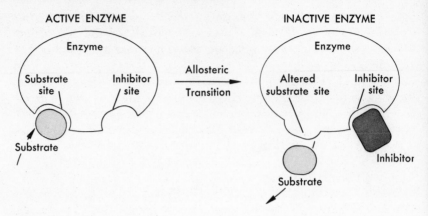

Figure 5·3. Allosteric transition. Normally the substrate must attach to the active site of an enzyme in a particular way for catalysis to occur. However, when an inhibitor (end product) is attached to its specific site, a structural transition in the enzyme occurs so that the normal substrate can no longer attach. This blocks the catalytic activity of an enzyme for a particular biosynthetic step.

analogues, such as 5-methyltryptophan. Normally the analogue serves (as does tryptophan) as a feedback inhibitor. Mutations affecting the inhibitor site exclusively might be expected to confer resistance to the analogue. Umbarger has also reported feedback-resistant mutants among revertants (back mutants) or ordinary auxotrophs.

Allosteric transitions provide an extremely flexible system for regulation. Certain enzymes have been shown to be activated by combination with an effector molecule that differs from the catalytic substrate. Particular enzymes may be activated by one metabolite and inhibited by another. Thus, an effector produced by one biosynthetic pathway could trigger the synthetic activity of another unrelated pathway.

Regulation of Enzyme Synthesis

Striking advances have been made during the past ten years in reaching an understanding of the regulatory mechanisms concerned with gene activity. These mechanisms affect the formation of enzymes that are the functional products of structural genes. From such studies has evolved the concept of the *operon*.

ENZYME INDUCTION AND REPRESSION

Bacteria have long been known to adapt to the presence of a new component of their environment. For example, after a short lag period, a bacterial population will undergo adaptation and gain the ability to ferment lactose. In this case, mutation followed by selection could be ruled out because essentially all the cells in a culture simultaneously develop the capacity to use the new substrate. When the question was examined, it became clear that adaptation of the culture was due to the synthesis of the enzyme β-galactosidase, which cleaves lactose. For several years, there remained some doubt as to whether the enzyme was newly synthesized or whether activity was unmasked from some inactive precursor. It finally became clear that indeed the presence of lactose resulted in the *de novo* synthesis of new enzyme molecules (Figure 5·4). This phenomenon eventually came to be known as enzyme *induction*.

Inducible enzymes increase in relative concentration in the presence of a new substrate (inducer) as much as ten thousandfold over the usual level. Mutants have been isolated that produce high levels of enzyme regardless of whether the inducer is present. Such mutants are called *constitutive* mutants. The enzymes formed by constitutive mutants are identical to those formed by induction.

Inducers are quite specific, although certain structural analogues that are not utilized may serve as inducers. Perhaps the most striking feature of induction, however, is the fact that an entire set of enzymes involved in the conversion of the substrate is coordinately induced by a single inducer. The most extensively studied case of enzyme induction is that involving lactose fermentation in *E. coli*. (This system will be discussed in detail when the Jacob-Monod operon hypothesis is discussed.)

Another regulatory phenomenon, one that results in the coordinate alteration of the activity of several enzymes, has been extensively studied. Vogel coined the term *enzyme repression* to describe the phenomenon by which exposure of cells to a particular substance re-

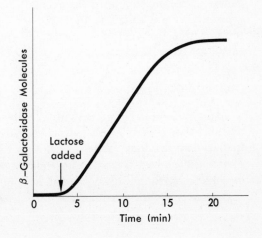

Figure 5·4. Enzyme induction. Following the addition of a new substrate (lactose), the relative amount of the enzyme β-galactosidase increases to a maximum level, which is maintained. β-galactosidase catalyzes the cleavage of lactose to its component sugars.

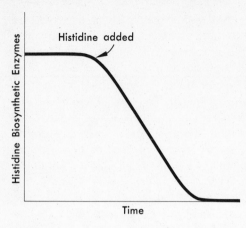

Figure 5·5. Enzyme repression. A growing culture of bacteria normally maintains a particular level of enzymes concerned with the biosynthesis of histidine. When histidine is added to the culture, further synthesis of these enzymes ceases; the relative amount will slowly decrease through time. If histidine is removed, new synthesis of these enzymes will resume.

sulted in a relative decrease in the rate of enzyme synthesis. The phenomenon is complementary to feedback inhibition in that the end product acts as the repressor of its own biosynthesis. However, in the case of enzyme repression, it is not enzymatic activity that is affected but rather enzyme *synthesis.* In other words, an end product regulates the synthesis of all enzymes leading to its own production. One regulatory process acts at the enzyme structural level and the other (as will be discussed later) acts at the gene level.

The addition of molecules such as amino acids (e.g., histidine) results in repression of all enzymes involved in the pathway leading to synthesis (Figure 5·5). This occurs even if a mutation in one gene in the pathway is present. Furthermore, a particular mutation will release the repression of the whole pathway. Such mutations have been isolated for several pathways including those leading to tryptophan, histidine, arginine, and isoleucine-leucine-valine. These mutations frequently map at locations distinct from the site of the structural genes controlling the particular enzyme in question. Genes that control repressibility are called *regulator genes,* in contrast to those that determine the amino acid sequence of enzyme molecules, which are called *structural genes.*

GENE CLUSTERING

Early mutational studies with *Neurospora* revealed a number of mutants that controlled the several steps in the biosynthesis of a particular end product. When such sets of mutants were genetically mapped, they were found to be widely scattered on the various chromosomes, showing only occasional close linkage relationships.

However, working with *Salmonella,* Demerec and his coworkers observed unique clusters of genes corresponding to the various enzymes of a biosynthetic pathway. In particular, the tryptophan and histidine pathways were shown to be clustered. The histidine pathway consisted of no fewer than ten enzymes converting phosphoribosyl pyrophosphate and ATP to the end product, histidine. The pathway of histidine biosynthesis does not have branches, and any mutant lacking any individual enzyme will grow on added histidine (Figure 5·6). The work of Ames, Hartman, and their colleagues over several years has resulted in the isolation of over one thousand histidine-requiring mutants. Fine-structure mapping shows the relationship between chromosomal regions corresponding to the sequence of enzymes in the biosynthetic pathway as indicated in Figure 5·6.

The group of clustered genes in the histidine system is subject to coordinate repression. If histidine is added to the growth medium, all enzymes decrease in activity, which suggests that the cluster of genes acts as a unit of function and regulation. Indeed, it has been demonstrated that an extremely large (polycistronic) mRNA that is absent in repressed cells is produced in constitutive cells.

THE THEORY OF THE OPERON

In 1961, Jacob and Monod presented a model to account for regulation of protein (enzyme) synthesis, particularly that involving induction or repression phenomena. Out of this model mechanism developed the theory of the operon.

Speculation was based primarily on the β-galactosidase enzyme system in *E. coli*. In this bacteria the ability to ferment the sugar lactose depends on two structural genes—*z*, which determines the structure of the enzyme β-galactosidase, and *y*, which determines the structure of β-galactoside permease, the protein involved in transport of lactose into the cell. The enzyme β-galactosidase splits the disaccharide lactose to glucose and galactose, its component six-carbon sugars. Mutants that fail to make this enzyme cannot utilize lactose as a carbon source. This is equally true of mutants that do not produce the permease, in this case because they are unable to concentrate lactose in the cell to be hydrolized intracellularly by β-galactosidase. (Permease mutants are called cryptic mutants because intact cells cannot but broken cells can hydrolyze lactose.)

Still a third gene *x* controls the synthesis of galactoside transacetylase, which is required for lactose utilization although its exact function is not clear. All three genes, *z*, *y*, and *x*, are called structural genes because they are known to be responsible for the structure of proteins (enzymes). All three structural genes, which are closely associated in

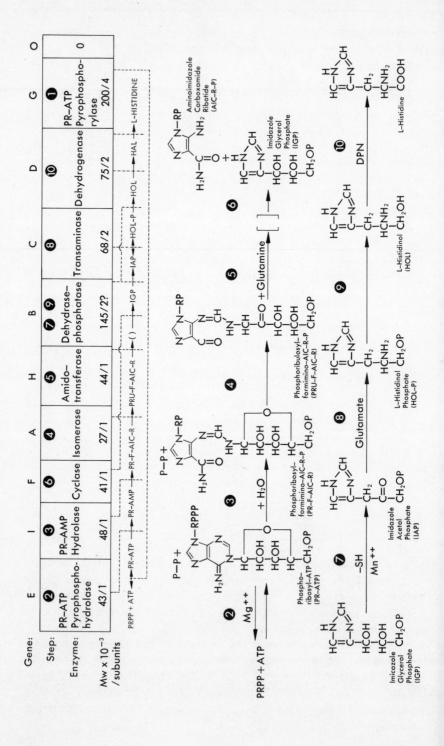

a cluster, plus a site called the operator (o) are collectively called the *lactose operon.* The operator site is located at the end of the z locus and distal to the x locus.

$$o \qquad z \qquad y \qquad x$$

Thus a cluster of genes that we now know to act in a coordinate fashion is arranged sequentially on the chromosome. All three enzymes corresponding to the three genes appear rapidly and simultaneously when their common substrate is presented to a cell population. Such a coordinate induction suggests a common control mechanism for all components of the operon. The operator site is the key to a coordinate regulatory process.

Investigators have for some time known of mutants that are not subject to the usual induction responses. They are called *constitutive mutants* and are characterized by a high level of all related enzymes, regardless of whether their substrate is present. It is now clear that constitutive mutants are of two genetic types. One set maps at one end of the z gene in the lactose operon in what is now known as the operator locus. Such mutants, o^c, have relative levels of all three enzymes characteristic of those found in the presence of an inducer. This suggests that the operator locus acts as some type of switch to turn on and off its set of three enzymes. A defective o locus leaves the switch on continuously.

A second set of constitutive mutants is located some distance from the lactose operon on the *E. coli* chromosome. This other gene (i) functions in the coordinate control of the lactose operon; it is called the regulator gene. Mutants at this locus (i^-) produce enzyme in the absence of inducer (lactose).

Even though mutations affecting either o or i locus may result in constitutive enzyme production, they can be distinguished one from the other. By setting up artificial heterozygotes (two chromosomes), it is possible to test dominance between o^+ and o^o as well as i^+ and i^-. Such heterozygotes of the type $\dfrac{o^+z^+y^+x^+}{o^cz^+y^+x^+}$ produce enzymes in a constitutive fashion. Indeed it is clear that the o locus can regulate

Figure 5·6. Biosynthesis of histidine. The structural formula represents the known intermediates in the synthesis of histidine in bacteria. The sequence of genes is represented by letters, with the operator site located on the extreme right. The name of each enzyme is indicated, with its position in the biosynthetic sequence represented by numbers. An abbreviated biosynthetic sequence is shown below the genetic map with the enzymatic site of control for each step. The molecular weight and number of subunits of the enzyme are shown below the name of the enzyme. [After Loper et al., Brookhaven Symp. in Biology 17, 15 (1964).]

genes only on the same chromosome (*cis*), because the genotype $\dfrac{o^+z^+y^+x^+}{o^cz^-y^-x^-}$ can produce enzyme only after induction, that is, the enzyme is not constitutive. It has been suggested that the operator site is nothing more than the initiation sequence of bases for transcription of mRNA from the operon.

The *i* locus is characterized by the fact that it can exert its expression in either chromosome regardless of whether it is linked. Heterozygotes $\dfrac{i^-;\,o^+z^+y^+x^+}{i^+;\,o^+z^-y^-x^-}$ are inductible, thus implying that the *i* gene product is cytoplasmic in nature.

These facts leave us with the concept of a set of structural genes all controlled by a common switch (the operator locus) that, in turn, is under the control of the product of another gene (the regulator locus). The operon model fits the observations concerning both enzyme induction and enzyme repression into a common mechanism involving gene regulating relationships.

It is presumed that all genes, both structural and regulatory, are transcribed into mRNA molecules. We know that structural genes form mRNA and, in turn, enzymes but only under rigidly defined conditions. When a substrate (inducer, e.g., lactose) is present, mRNAs and enzymes are formed that convert the substrate to some product. When an end product (corepressor, e.g., histidine) is absent, mRNAs and enzymes are formed for the synthesis of the end product. Thus, the ultimate control is at the level of formation of mRNAs corresponding to the genetic region in question. Such control is accomplished through the products of regulatory genes, which have come to be called *repressors*.

Repressors, the product of regulatory genes, control the rate of mRNA synthesis, presumably by combining with DNA at the operator site. When repressors are combined at the *o* site, the operon is not switched on and no mRNA is transcribed. This is the case when either the regulator gene or the operator site is defective through mutation. It is also the case when sufficient end product (e.g., histidine) is present. Presumably, the corepressor, histidine, combines with the repressor, thus preventing the repressor's attachment to DNA and leaving the operon switch open. When histidine disappears (derepression) the free repressor combines with *o* and closes the switch. Inducers such as lactose also combine with repressor molecules, making them inactive or incapable of attachment to *o* site.

It appears, then, that regulator genes produce some product that has some affinity for DNA at a specific operator site. When this happens, that block of DNA within that particular operon cannot be transcribed to mRNA. An inducer prevents this attachment and a corepressor enhances it. Such a relationship is summarized in Figure 5·7. Only recently has a repressor been isolated and identified as a protein.

The concept of the operon's regulating protein synthesis (as proposed by Jacob and Monod and periodically updated) still explains the greatest number of observations. Umbarger (1964) has summarized the several properties of the protein-synthesizing system, all of which the operon model takes into account.

(1) DNA serves as the primary source of instructions for protein synthesis and it is DNA that is uniquely transmitted from cell generation to cell generation.

(2) The information in DNA is transcribed into RNA by means

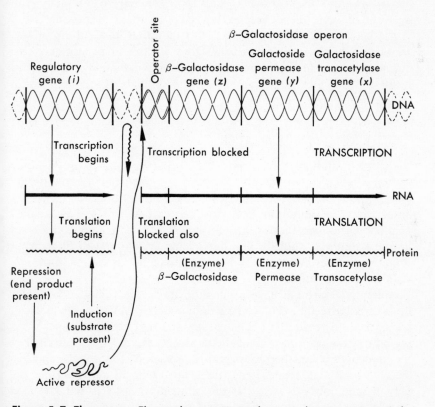

Figure 5·7. The operon. The regulatory gene produces a substance (repressor) that is capable of blocking transcription of DNA to mRNA for a particular genetic region (the operon). The repressor is an active blocking agent when the end product (corepressor) of the biosynthetic sequence is present to combine with it. The presence of an inducer (e.g., lactose) favors the inactive form of the transcription blocking agent (repressor), resulting in normal transcription and subsequent translation of all enzymes needed to utilize the substrate, thus depleting the cell of the inducing agent. [After Jacob and Monod, in *J. Molec. Biol.*, 3:318, 1961, p. 344.]

of an enzyme (RNA polymerase) that produces a single-stranded, mRNA that is complementary to one of the DNA strands.

(3) The region of DNA transcribed into a single message may contain instructions for the synthesis of several proteins (polycistronic mRNA) of particular tRNA molecules that are unique.

(4) Translation of a particular sequence of bases in mRNA into a particular sequence of amino acids in a protein (enzyme) is mediated on the ribosome and with the involvement of specific tRNA molecules carrying their own unique amino acid.

(5) A particular DNA sequence cannot be transcribed to mRNA under certain unique conditions. These conditions involve the interaction of a product of a regulator gene (repressor) with the initiation site (*o*) in that DNA sequence. This repressor may require activation by a small molecule (corepressor) such as the end product of a biosynthetic sequence (repression). On the other hand, the repressor may be unable to interact with the DNA when a small molecule (inducer), such as the substrate of a reaction (induction), is present. Either repression or induction occurs as coordinate events involving a multigene region.

POLARITY MUTATIONS: MODULATION

Certain mutations have been isolated, particularly in the histidine operon, that have two effects. Not only is a particular enzymatic activity lost but there is a relative decrease in all enzymes coded by genes distal from the mutation from the operator site. These are called *polarity mutations;* they constitute almost half of a large number of histidine mutants studied. The loss in activity was 10 to 50 percent of normal values in genes distal to the site of the mutation—but *only* distal genes were affected.

Ames and Hartman have proposed a model providing a molecular basis of polarity that they call *modulation.* It requires one messenger per operon, the reading of the message as a unit, and ribosomes starting only at the operator end of the messenger RNA. At any given time the messenger is attached to several ribosomes. When a particular cistron has been read (translated), the protein falls off and the ribosome may or may not be released. If the ribosome is not released, the next gene in sequence is read. The model proposes that particular coding triplets that occur at the beginning of each gene determine whether the ribosome is released. These triplets, called *modulating triplets,* code for rare and unusual tRNA molecules that do not insert an amino acid but act only as regulatory agents. The model further suggests that a polarity mutant transforms a normal triplet into a modulating triplet.

The concept of induction and repression of enzyme synthesis is really concerned with control of RNA synthesis by DNA. DNA specifies RNA structure and, in that sense, regulates its synthesis. However, other mechanisms exist that regulate *rates* of RNA synthesis; it is with these processes that the present discussion is concerned.

It is clear that a mechanism exists through which coordination of RNA and protein synthesis occurs. Ribosomes, which constitute the major part of cellular RNA, are certainly involved with protein synthesis and their synthetic rate is reduced when protein synthesis is inhibited. If the growth of a bacterial culture is stimulated by shifting the cells to a richer medium, the synthesis of RNA is stimulated in preference to DNA or protein synthesis. The effect on increased synthesis of RNA is almost immediate, while that of protein involves a lag period. This suggests that the main limitation on rates of protein synthesis is RNA.

One of the most striking observations implicating amino acids (the precursors of protein) in regulation of RNA syntheses was made using auxotrophs of *E. coli*. Such strains carried genetic lesions and were incapable of synthesizing particular (e.g., methionine) amino acids that were required as a supplement in the minimal growth medium. If such cells are grown on the amino acid, then washed and transferred to a minimal medium, growth stops almost at once. However, RNA synthesis halts as rapidly as does that of protein. Furthermore, if protein synthesis is partially inhibited by the antibiotic Chloramphenicol, RNA is still synthesized—but only if all required amino acids are supplied.

Although a full complement of amino acids might be required for the synthesis of a special protein, other theories are more prominent. It has been suggested that amino acids induce RNA synthesis by combining with their respective tRNAs—any one of which is capable of repressing RNA synthesis.

A number of years ago, Borek and his coworkers discovered a mutant that continued to synthesize RNA even when it was deprived of its required amino acid, methionine. This mutant was referred to as relaxed (RC^{rel}) while the parental strain was called straight (RC^{st}). Genetic studies showed that the gene bore no relationship to the particular amino acid requirement but is relaxed no matter what growth-essential amino acid is withdrawn. However, the RC^{rel} strain only exhibits unusual RNA synthetic ability under conditions of amino acid deprivation.

With strain RC^{rel} it has been shown that RNA formed under the above-mentioned relaxed conditions appears in so-called relaxed particles that seem to be deficient in ribosomal protein. Complete ribosomes are formed when the missing amino acid is supplied. Preferential synthesis of ribosomal protein occurs, probably on mature ribosomes, with subsequent transfer to relaxed particles, at which point the particles are converted to mature, functional ribosomes.

In summary, the presently available information is consistent with the general model of regulation proposed by Maaløe and Kurland several years ago. They suggested that amino acids act as inducers of RNA synthesis but that a special protein is required for completion of ribosomes. Certainly tRNA molecules play a central role in the regulatory process.

Histone Regulation of Gene Activity

Miescher, who discovered DNA almost one hundred years ago, also discovered a group of proteins that were closely associated with DNA called histones. They are basic proteins containing a considerable amount of lysine and arginine, but other amino acids are totally missing or extremely low in concentration. In general, histones can be further separated into four major and separable groups, although many different proteins make up each group. Another feature of histone structure is the unusual spacing of the basic amino acids contained therein. Many lysine doublets occur, but they are spaced at irregular intervals along the chain.

When histone and DNA are mixed, histones become bound to DNA—forming what is called nucleohistones. Under special conditions, what appears to be a natural reconstitution of native nucleohistone occurs. It was with such material that Huang and Bonner studied the ability of nucleohistones to support DNA-dependent RNA synthesis with pea-embryo preparations. Purified RNA polymerase was incubated with labeled ribose triphosphates, and DNA either combined with nucleohistone or as pure (protein-free) DNA. DNA alone supported RNA synthesis; certain nucleohistones prevent the synthesis of RNA.

Additional experiments were carried out with a specific product protein: the globulin of pea cotyledons. This protein is a reserve product not synthesized in buds or roots but only in the developing cotyledons. A cell-free system coupling DNA-dependent RNA synthesis and the RNA-dependent ribosomal-protein synthesis system was employed. The specific globulin was synthesized only when DNA from cotyledons was supplied; synthesis did not occur in response to other chromatins. However, when the histone is removed from bud chromatin, the free DNA is capable of supporting cotyledon globulin synthesis. Presumably, the gene(s) for globulin synthesis, though present in tissues other than cotyledons, is repressed by the presence of a particular histone. Indeed, when the histone is added back to DNA, the ability of DNA to synthesize globulin is again lost from either bud or cotyledon. Bonner concludes that histones are agents of gene repression. The exact mechanism of action, however, remains unanswered.

The Regulatory Role of Hormones

The regulatory role of hormones in the development and activities of higher plants and animals is well known. However, it has been only in recent years that evidence has been accumulated to suggest that the site of primary action is very near the gene. The best evidence suggests that at least some hormones act on the synthesis of RNA—perhaps mRNA.

$$DNA \xrightarrow{\text{hormones}} RNA \longrightarrow Protein$$

Such a conclusion is based, in part, on the action of actinomycin D on hormone function. Actinomycin D inhibits the DNA-stimulated synthesis of RNA (transcription). The difficulty in evaluating this effect is due to the phenotypic effect such an inhibitory agent exerts in higher organisms.

Armstrong has suggested a more specific site of action for plant auxins (hormones) in nucleic acid biosynthesis. His hypothesis is based on a model for quantitative regulation of total RNA synthesis in bacteria. The bacterial system is dependent for RNA synthesis on the available supply of amino acids. Free tRNA molecules have been suggested as being the repressors. With the formation of aminoacyl-tRNA, repression occurs and RNA synthesis proceeds. Presumably, in plants, there would occur a tRNA specific for auxin. Charging of this tRNA with auxin would result in an induction of RNA synthesis. It has been further suggested that auxin tRNA may serve as the signal for chain initiation during translation, a role that has been demonstrated for N-formylmethionine-tRNA in bacteria.

Bonner has hypothesized that hormones work by derepressing genes previously repressed, thus allowing the synthesis of mRNA molecules. Even the knowledge that hormones act at or near the gene level may provide a major breakthrough into the problem of differentiation.

References

Ames, B. N., and R. G. Martin. "Biochemical Aspects of Genetics: The Operon," *Ann. Rev. Biochem. 33:* 235, 1964.
Atkinson, Daniel E. "Biological Feedback Control at the Molecular Level," *Science 150:* 851, 1965.

Bonner, D. M. (ed.). *Control Mechanisms in Cellular Processes,* New York: Ronald, 1960.

Cohen, G. N. "Regulation of Enzyme Activity in Microorganisms," *Ann. Rev. Microbiol. 19:* 105, 1965.

Jacob, F., and J. Monod. "Genetic Regulatory Mechanisms in the Synthesis of Proteins," *J. Mol. Biol. 3:* 318, 1961.

Loper, T. C., M. Grabner, R. C. Stahl, Z. Hartman, and Phillip E. Hartman. "Subunit Structure of Proteins: Biochemical and Genetic Aspects," *Brookhaven Symp. in Biology 17:* 15, 1964.

Maas, W. K., and E. McFall. "Genetic Aspects of Metabolic Control," *Ann. Rev. Microbiol. 18:* 95, 1964.

Monod, J., J. P. Changeaux, and F. Jacob. "Allosteric Proteins and Cellular Control Systems," *J. Mol. Biol. 6:* 306, 1963.

Monod, J., J. Wyman, and J. P. Changeaux. "On the Nature of Allosteric Transitions: A Plausible Model," *J. Mol. Biol. 12:* 88, 1965.

Neidhardt, F. C. "The Regulation of RNA Synthesis in Bacteria," *Prog. Nucleic Acid Res. 4:* 145, 1964.

Stadtman, E. R. "Enzyme Multiplicity and Function in the Regulation of Divergent Metabolic Pathways," *Bact. Rev. 27:* 170, 1963.

Stent, G. S. "The Operon: On Its Third Anniversary," *Science 144:* 816, 1964.

Umbarger, H. E. "The Integration of Metabolic Pathways," *Ann. Rev. Plant Physiol. 14:* 19, 1963.

Umbarger, H. E. "Intercellular Regulatory Mechanisms," *Science 145:* 674, 1964.

Genetic Recombination: Its Mode
and Mechanism in Microorganisms

GREGOR MENDEL, in his studies with the garden pea, focused his attention on a limited number of characteristics that could be easily followed in the offspring of hybridization experiments. He postulated the existence of unit factors that distributed themselves in a random fashion in progeny. Shortly after the rediscovery of Mendel's observations, Bateson and Punnett in England observed the first exception to Mendelian principles. The phenomenon of nonindependent assortment was referred to as *linkage* and was soon further defined by Morgan and his group at Columbia University. Sturtevant showed that genes could be arranged in linkage groups on the basis of frequency of recombination, and he established the first chromosome map. Thus, each chromosome of higher organisms can be represented as a linear arrangement of genes linked one to the other that undergo exchanges with homologous chromosomes during the meiotic process that gives rise to gametes. The strength of linkage appeared to be roughly a function of physical proximity of one gene to another. This concept was supported by the direct observation (by Painter and Stone) of banding patterns in the giant salivary chromosomes of *Drosophila*.

Griffith's discovery, in 1928, of bacterial-transforming principles was a link to the molecular and Avery, MacLeod, and McCarthy in 1944 identified the chemical involved as nucleic acid. Since that time, Lederberg demonstrated recombination in bacteria as well as the virus-mediated phenomenon of transduction. These discoveries will be discussed in some detail because they provide considerable insight into recombination at the molecular level. Once this background has been developed, the more complex problem of recombination in chromosomal systems will be briefly readdressed.

Conjugation in Bacteria

The transfer of genetic material by means of direct cellular contact between a donor and a recipient bacterium is called *conjugation;* it was discovered by Lederberg and Tatum in 1946. Secondary to cell contact, actual chromosome transfer occurs; the process is unique to bacterial conjugation and is vastly different from chromosome transfer in higher organisms.

Three observations suggested the unusual nature of recombination in bacteria. If a number of genetic markers is present in the donor strain, not all markers are transferred to the recipient strain. Furthermore, reciprocal recombinant markers are not recovered—as would be expected if both conjugating cells contributed equally, as occurs with recombination involving sperm and eggs. Finally, linkage (map) relationships varied with different strains used.

The discovery of bacterial strains that yield one thousand times more recombinants provided much to our knowledge of the mechanism of conjugation. As was later discovered, these strains, called Hfr (high frequency of recombination), contain an autonomous, transmittible element called F (fertility) or sex factor. Thus male (donor) cells were F^+ and female (recipient) cells F^-; rarely, an F^+ cell is converted to Hfr, resulting in an enormous increase in recombination frequency.

The F factor, therefore, resembles an infective element, now called an *episome,* that can spread throughout a population of F^- cells. It may be lost spontaneously but never acquired by mutation; it is acquired only by conjugation.

Ten years after the discovery of recombination in bacteria, Jacob and Wollman proposed that the bacterial chromosome is a closed or circular structure. Hence all genes are linked to all other genes, thus accounting for the linkage data. More recently, Cairns was able to isolate intact *E. coli* chromosomes consisting of DNA molecules connected end to end that are approximately 900 μ in length. Rarely, an F particle in an F^+ cell becomes attached to the (circular) chromosome at one of several possible sites, thus converting it to an Hfr cell. The attachment results in breakage of the circular chromosome so that high frequency of recombination is associated with linear chromosomal systems and not with the circular stage. Furthermore, when this occurs the F factor is no longer autonomous but has integrated with the bacterial genome and is transferred (rarely) to recipient cells just as any other bacterial genetic marker (Figure 6·1).

The oriented, partial transfer of the Hfr chromosome was demonstrated in an elegantly simple experiment performed by Jacob and Wollman. Hfr cells carrying several known genetic markers were in-

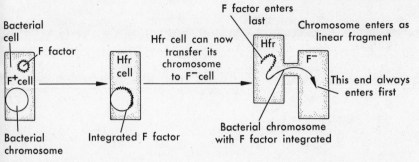

Figure 6·1. Formation of an Hfr cell from an F+ cell by integration of free F factor into the bacterial chromosome. F+ cells are formed from F− cells by the infection of the latter by free F factors. If and when the F factor becomes integrated into the chromosome, that cell becomes Hfr and capable of recombination (with high frequency) with F cells.

cubated for varying lengths of time; the mating was then interrupted by dropping aliquots into a Waring blender. The action of the blender broke the conjugation bridge (and thus the partially transferred chromosome), but the cells survived the treatment. The various samples were then plated onto growth media that allowed the detection of the various markers used (Figure 6·2).

Under ideal conditions the entire chromosome is transferred in approximately one hundred minutes from the male to the female cell (Table 6·1). However, under usual conditions of natural agitation, the conjugation bridge is broken and the tail of the chromosome is not transferred. Only when the entire chromosome is transferred does the Hfr enter the recipient cell, thus the Hfr factor must determine the orientation of the transfer process.

TABLE 6·1

Genetic Map of the Chromosomal Segment Injected with High Frequency in One Strain of Hfr

	thr	leu	azi	T_1	lac_1	gal	
A *	—	—	90	70	40	25	15
B †	8	8½	9	11	18	25	26

[From Jacob and Wollman. *The Biological Replication of Macromolecules,* New York: Academic, 1958, p. 75.]

* A is the percentage of thr+, leu+, and str-r recombinants that have inherited the different Hfr alleles.

† B is the time in minutes at which individual Hfr characters start penetrating the F− recipient.

With various Hfr strains, the lead marker may vary as the *F* factor breaks the circular chromosome at different genetic sites. In fact, the

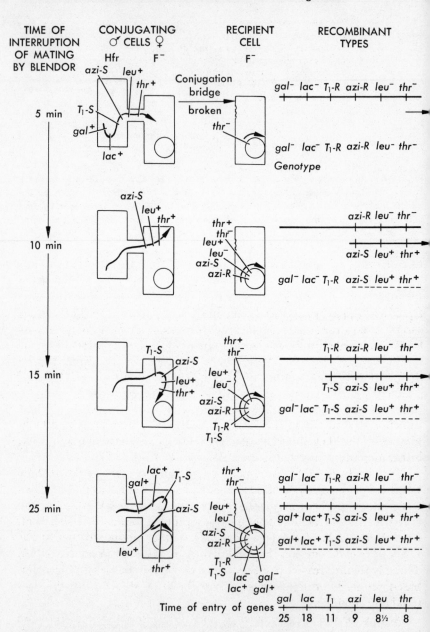

Figure 6·2. Interrupted mating experiment. Conjugating *E. coli* cells of Hfr and F− types are interrupted in their mating process by breaking the conjugation bridge at different times. Progressively larger donor chromosome fragments are transferred with increasing time. This temporal process is measured by determining the presence of various recombinant types representing genes contributed by the donor (Hfr) cells.

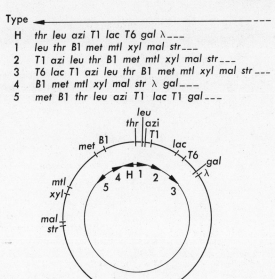

Type
H   thr leu azi T1 lac T6 gal λ___
1   leu thr B1 met mtl xyl mal str___
2   T1 azi leu thr B1 met mtl xyl mal str___
3   T6 lac T1 azi leu thr B1 met mtl xyl mal str___
4   B1 met mtl xyl mal str λ gal___
5   met B1 thr leu azi T1 lac T1 gal___

Figure 6·3. Orders of genes in varying Hfr strains. Both the lead gene and directionality of the chromosome vary in different Hfr types. The first marker gene transferred is indicated on the left by the arrow. The circle indicates the approximate and relative location of the marker genes. Again the arrow indicates the first portion of the chromosome transferred during conjugation. [After F. Jacob, and E. L. Wollman, in Soc. Exptl. Biol., 12:75, 1957, and after Hayes, 1964.]

direction of transfer may reverse, indicating further that the attachment of *F*, rather than the directionality of the chromosome itself, is the orientating factor (Figure 6·3).

Chemically, the *F* factor appears to be DNA containing about three times 10^5 base pairs, which is about the size of a bacterial virus (bacteriophage) or about 2 percent of the amount of DNA in the *E. coli* chromosome. A fraction of the DNA contains an unusual GC content, whereas the bulk of the DNA has GC content similar to that of the DNA in *E. coli*—in fact, half will hybridize with chromosomal DNA. There is further reason to believe that the *F* element is itself circular, based primarily on the results of recombination studies with the bacterial chromosome.

Models for the integration of *F* and the bacterial chromosome are based primarily on studies with a related episome (phage) λ which will be discussed later. However, it is suggested that regions of homology exist between *F* and the chromosome, i.e., regions at which pairing occurs just as between homologous regions of homologous chromosomes. Such pairing is rare but once it occurs a breakage re-

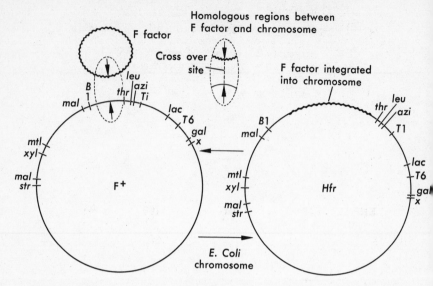

Figure 6·4. Crossover insertion of F factor into an E. coli chromosome. Regions of homology between the F factor and the chromosome result in pairing, followed by a breakage-reunion recombination event. This results in the incorporation of the (autonomous) F factor into the chromosome (integration). Such a cell is thus converted from F+ to Hfr.

union (crossover) recombination occurs between the two circular units, giving as a product a single circular unit undergoing synchronous replication (Figure 6·4).

Chromosomal replication appears to be an essential component in the transfer of the chromosome of Hfr strains. Replication appears to start at one point on the chromosome, which site is called the *replicator* (Figure 6·5). The replicator may well serve as a molecular swivel for the unwinding of the two old complementary strands during replication. Replicators probably occur in all circular DNA structures (such as *F* factor). Once *F* has integrated into the chromosome by crossover, the *F* replicator assumes the dominant role in subsequent replications. There is evidence that the replicator, or at least regions of the chromosome, are intimately associated with the cell membrane. This may account for the formation of specific receptor sites that are characteristic of Hfr cells and that are involved in the formation of the conjugation bridge.

Two models relating chromosome replication to chromosome transfer into the recipient cell have been proposed (Figure 6·6). Jacob and Brenner suggest that the *F* replicator serves as an initiation point for replication and one of the daughter chromosomes penetrates the female cell at the expense of the replication process. Thus the repli-

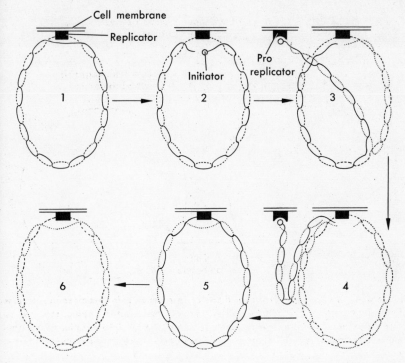

Figure 6·5. Replication of a chromosome in *E. coli*. [From Lark, K. G., in *Bact. Rev., 30: 29,* 1966.]

cator, which is part of the *F* factor, is synthesized last and would enter last. On the other hand, Bouck and Adelberg point to data suggesting that the origin (first locus transferred) is the last to be synthesized. They further propose a model in which a replicating chromosome fails to undergo ring closure, suggesting that it is this unit that is subsequently transferred (but in an orientated fashion) following DNA synthesis. The latter model leaves the orientation of transfer still unexplained. Quite recently several groups of workers have supplied compelling support to the former model (in which the chromosome is replicated as it is transferred). This process, though unresolved in detail, clearly depends on chromosomal replication and probably implies a fundamental role for the membrane in both replication and conjugation in bacteria.

Transduction

Transduction involves the transfer of small fragments of DNA from one bacterial cell to another by means of a phage. The infective phage carries—inside a protein coat and along with its own genome—a

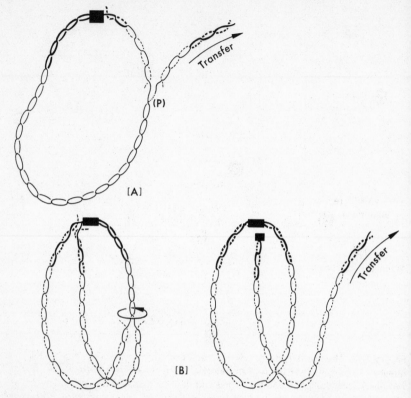

Figure 6·6. Models for chromosome transfer. A: Jacob-Brenner model. **B:** Bouck-Adelberg model. [From Adelberg, E. A., and J. Pittard, *Bact. Rev.* 29: 161, 1965, pp. 164, 165.]

DNA fragment derived from its previous host. The transducing phage (carrying the foreign DNA) represents a very small fraction (one per million) of those released from a host cell.

Two types of transduction occur: one involves what appears to be a random choice of genetic markers from the host (general transduction); the other (restricted transduction) involves particular genetic sites. (The latter case has already been mentioned in reference to the *F* factor, which appears to have homology with particular genetic loci in recipient cells.)

Transduction was discovered in *Salmonella* by Zinder and Lederberg in 1952. Zinder, a student of Lederberg, was studying various strains and mutants to see if recombination would occur. In several combinations, particularly high frequencies of recombination occurred. A simple experiment was performed to rule out the conjugation that required direct cell contact, which had been recently discovered. When high recombinant (transducing) strains were maintained in a

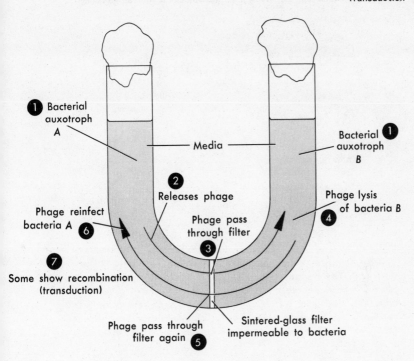

Figure 6·7. The transduction experiment of Zinder and Lederberg. A high frequency of recombination occurs between two cell types (A and B) when the bacterial cells themselves are physically separated and thus not capable of conjugation. A filterable agent passes from one cell to another, transferring genes between them. This phenomenon is called transduction; a phage serves as the vector for genetic transfer between bacterial cells.

U tube (physically separated by means of a fine sintered-glass filter), prototrophs were still recovered (Figure 6·7). Thus, it later became clear that one of the strains released a phage (P_{22}) that could transverse the filter and infect cells in the other end of the U tube. These cells would ultimately lyse, releasing phage that carried additional fragments of DNA derived from one host cell; the phage in turn reinfected the original population. Occasionally these reinfections resulted in an altered genotype reflecting loci present in the lysed cell population. When isolated, the filterable agent had all the properties of a phage, including insensitivity to DNase. In addition, the DNA fragment it then carried appeared to be fully integrated with the phage genome.

Prior to a further discussion of transduction, the phenomenon of lysogeny (Figure 6·8) must be sketched. Infection of a bacterium with a bacteriophage leads to one of two alternatives. The phage may multiply, mature, and ultimately lyse the host cell. Or, certain phage

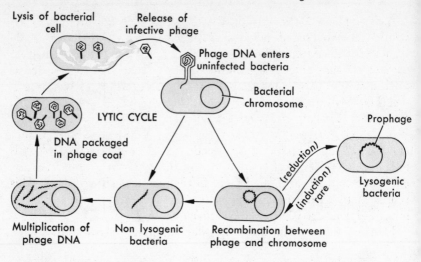

Figure 6·8. The lysogenic cycle of a temperate phage. A phage will normally replicate, become packaged into a protective coat, and lyse the cell—releasing free phage that infect other cells. Occasionally the phage recombines with the bacterial chromosome and replicates as part of the circular chromosome (prophage); occasionally, but rarely, the prophage is released, initiating the lytic cycle again.

(temperate) may produce in the host an immunity that prevents multiplication of the phage and lysis of the bacterial cell. Such an association is called the *lysogenic state;* in it, the bacterial genome and the phage genome (prophage) persist together indefinitely. A lysogenic bacterial cell can be induced to release vegetative phage by various factors, such as exposure to ultraviolet light. Such treatment results in resumption of the infective cycle once again.

SPECIALIZED TRANSDUCTION WITH BACTERIOPHAGE λ

Shortly after the discovery of transduction, the Lederbergs reported the properties of a bacteriophage (λ) for which *E. coli* (K_{12}) was lysogenic—the λ prophage could become integrated with the host genome. This phage is located in a particular position in the bacterial chromosome; it can be mapped as can any other locus and it is reproduced by the same processes involved in chromosomal replication.

Genetic defects have been induced in λ and such mutant phage are unable to carry out a particular function of the lytic cycle. These mutants are called *defective* phage; the nondefective ones are called *active*. Other mutants are available that permit genetic crosses. An extensive linkage map has been built from such recombination analysis.

Bacteriophage λ can transduce a cluster of loci that are concerned with the metabolism of galactose. However, when λ is grown lytically on bacteria carrying the wild-type (gal⁺) markers, no transduction occurs; it occurs only with a culture of gal⁺ bacterial lysogenic for λ. Such a culture can be induced (with ultraviolet light) to lyse, and it will infect a gal⁻ culture, producing, at low frequency, a gal⁺ colony. It appears that gal⁺ genes transferred by λ substitute for and replace their homologues in the recipient chromosome. In addition, another class of recombinants occurs; instead of replacing their homologous region, these recombinants are added to the recipient genome, that is, gal⁻, gal⁺, and λ are now present in the recipient chromosome. This results in two gal loci, the equivalent of a diploid condition. Such limited diploids have been named *syngenotes* by Morse.

Further studies with these transducing phages showed that they

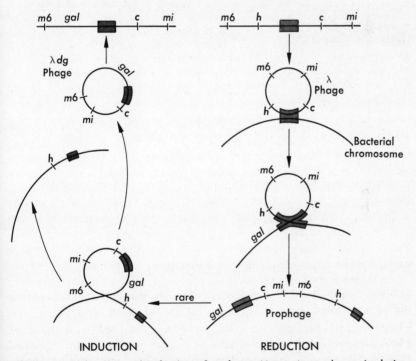

Figure 6·9. Reduction and induction of λ phage. Vegetative λ phage circularizes, synapses with a homologous region of the bacterial chromosome, and recombines (crosses over). This results in the incorporation of the phage into the bacterial chromosome, where it may persist (as prophage) indefinitely. Rarely a circle may cross out of the chromosome, releasing the phage. Often crossover occurs in such a way that the λ phage leaves behind (in the bacterial chromosome) part of its DNA and may include adjoining genes belonging to the bacteria. Such a phage is said to be defective (λdg). [After F. W. Stahl, *The Mechanics of Inheritance*, Englewood Cliffs: Prentice-Hall, Inc., 1964, p. 139.]

were themselves defective in part of their genome. It was as though they had left part of their own genome behind when the gal$^+$ marker was picked up from the host. Such transducing phage are called λ dg (defective galactose). As much as 25 percent of the phage DNA has been substituted by host DNA in certain λ dg–transducing particles.

The presently accepted model for lysogeny, transduction, and the formation of defective phage involves recombination between two circular DNA units (Figure 6·9). When the prophage undergoes lysogeny, it does so by pairing and recombination between the circular chromosome of the phage and the bacterial host. The process is reversed when release of lytic phage is induced by ultraviolet irradiation. However, this process may result in loss of λ DNA and inclusion of some of the adjoining genetic region, namely, gal. Thus, the transducing phage that is produced carries part of the bacterial chromosome but has lost part of its own genome and is thus defective. However, it has great homing characteristics for the gal locus and quite effectively transduces that particular genetic region.

GENERAL TRANSDUCTION

As mentioned earlier, generalized transduction does not involve particular loci but rather random selection of markers from the host cell. But in this case, as in the case discussed above, it is likely that the transducing phage is itself defective, having substituted some of the host DNA into its structure.

Transduction has been used extensively in genetic analysis, particularly with gene clusters characteristic of operons (such as the histidine system in *Salmonella*). Gene fine-structure analysis has been a major contribution of transduction recombinational studies. Indeed, Yanofsky has demonstrated recombination within the triplet coding unit for a single amino acid—the ultimate in recombination analysis.

An unusual type of transduction occurs, called *abortive transduction,* in which the bacterial DNA is carried by the phage into the recipient cell. The DNA expresses itself functionally but does not become integrated into the host genome, nor does it replicate. It is actually a far less rare event than is complete transduction.

The phenomenon of abortive transduction was first noted in transduction involving the motile character in bacteria. If nonmotile bacteria are transduced with motile-derived DNA, occasional trails of colonies form off the side of the nonmotile colony. This represents the path of a single motile cell that produces nonmotile progeny at each cell division. The motile cell contains a free fragment of DNA derived from the motile bacteria; this DNA is fully expressed but is passed along in a random fashion to progeny cells.

Abortive transduction has been exploited for gene fine-structure analysis using more conventional nutritional mutants. It has been particularly valuable in testing identity or nonidentity of independently isolated mutants of similar phenotypes. By abortive transduction it has been possible to produce the equivalent of heterozygotes. Such heterozygotes, or artificial diploids, have been used for studies of the phenomenon of complementation. This phenomenon, which will be discussed later, involves a recombination between gene products.

The evolutionary implications of transduction provide fruitful ground for speculation. One wonders how genetic homologies between the bacterial and phage genome may have arisen. Certainly there is evidence of exchange of the bacterial chromosome into the genome of the phage and the reverse incorporation of phage DNA into the bacterial chromosome. Whereas such recombinational exchanges may be of some immediate disadvantage, they do provide raw material (DNA) for future evolution of both genomes. This is indeed a level of exchange superseding the usual rules of recombination within a species or species group. Recombinational exchange actually occurs between a bacterium and a virus. One wonders if such exchange might not occur between so-called somatic cells of higher organisms.

Genetic Transformation

Transformation is a phenomenon from which was derived the earliest definite evidence that DNA is the primary genetic material. (These early studies are described in Chapter 1.) In general, transformation may now be described as intercellular transfer of a fragment of the DNA from the donor genome, which fragment, through a process of recombination, replaces a particular nucleotide sequence of the recipient's genome. The phenomenon can be recognized only when that particular fragment from the donor is sufficiently different from the region replaced in the recipient to be detected as a change in characteristics (phenotype) of the cell progeny.

The size of the DNA fragment effective in transformation is fairly large in terms of molecular size (with a molecular weight of 1 million or greater) but represents only a small fraction of the recipient genome (less than 0.5 percent). This means that for every bacterium making effective contact with one DNA fragment, two hundred such contacts would have to be made before a particular genetic marker would be involved. Thus, it is not surprising that the frequency of transformation in recipient cells is low, usualy less than 1 percent. With a particular DNA sample, the numbers of transformants is a function of DNA concentration up to a saturating concentration. The fact that the frequency of transformation is very low at such a concentration of

ests that competition occurs between DNA molecules for
eceptor sites. This may be further demonstrated by the
f homologous but nontransforming DNA from recipient

mation requires a particular physiological state that is
transient in nature. Environmental conditions and, in particular,
culture media influence this state, called *competence,* and its duration
is restricted to a fraction of the cell's growth cycle. Thus, as one might
expect, those conditions required to attain a competent state vary
radically with different species. The presence of DNA does not of itself
induce competence.

It is likely that some change involving localized regions of the cell
wall or membrane determines competency. Normally, inhibitors that
interfere with protein synthesis will prevent the development of competence. In some cases, macromolecular fractions that may be washed
from cultures of competent cells induce competence in cells in earlier
stages of the culture cycle. With other species, such factors are more
elusive. A further complicating problem is the occasional presence of
DNAase in the culture medium, which would be expected to interfere with the transformation process. All these factors make it extremely difficult to show beyond doubt that a genetic barrier to
transformation in a particular species exists. Much effort has been
expended in attempts to demonstrate the phenomenon in higher organisms. As yet no fully documented and dependably reproducible
system has been developed for transformation in cell forms other than
bacteria.

Even in competent cell populations, various stages have been recognized in the transformation process. The earliest step involves the
penetration of DNA, which is believed to occur in two stages. The
first, a binding step, is reversible and probably involves only a physical
orientation of the long DNA molecule. The more important step is
irreversible and energy dependent, resulting in loss of DNA sensitivity
to DNAase. Stuy, in his studies with *Hemophilus influenzae,* has
shown the presence of two sites for penetration of DNA—corresponding well with the two membrane-associated replication sites that are
characteristic of certain bacteria. However, other studies suggest more
than two uptake sites.

DNA of rather high molecular weight appears to be required for
transformation. In general, double-stranded DNA is far more effective
than denatured, single-stranded DNA. It has been suggested that in
the pneumococcal system, the double-stranded structure is degraded
(by DNAase) to single-stranded DNA during penetration. If in this
system only single-stranded DNA enters, this would explain the brief
eclipse period in which no transforming activity can be recovered.

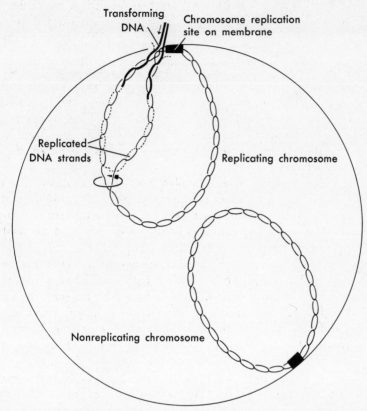

Figure 6·10. Hypothetical model for integration of transforming DNA into the replicating recipient chromosome. The bacterial chromosome is replicated at a site on the membrane (replicator). Transforming DNA enters at this point; when the homologous genetic region reaches the replicator site, the DNA is incorporated into the new chromosome. This may involve crossover or direct insertion at the growing point. Transforming strands may be incorporated into one or both newly synthesized strands. The two sites for DNA entry would, on the basis of this model, correspond to the two replicator sites for the two chromosomes.

Following the penetration stage, another two-step process is believed to occur. First there is an association between transforming DNA and the homologous region in the recipient chromosome. This would presumably be analogous to synapsis between like chromosomes during meiosis in higher organisms. The second step would involve actual integration, by recombination, of part of the transforming DNA with the recipient chromosome. In both these steps, biologically active (transforming) DNA can be recovered. A particularly appealing model for the integration process (Figure 6·10) has been developed by Bodmer. The model depends on a stationary replicating point for the chromosome that is located on the membrane. The transplanted DNA in a competent cell becomes associated with the homologous genetic region as it rotates past the stationary replicating point on the membrane. Bodmer suggests that replication is interrupted at that particular (homologous) region and the transforming DNA recombines when chromosomal DNA synthesis is resumed. This model would not require the DNA to pass through the cytoplasm and to seek out the homologous region through chance contact and pairing. Instead, the transport sites would be closely associated with the stationary replicating site through which all regions of the chromosomes would ultimately pass. Recombination could occur with either the old or new stand on either side of the replicating fork.

The evidence that transforming DNA does not produce a phenotypic effect prior to integration into the recipient chromosome is in accord with the above model. That is, transforming DNA is never free in the cytoplasm but is localized on the membrane at the site of the circular chromosome attachment. This is in contrast to the concept that DNA is brought in by a phage during transduction and is phenotypically expressed without integration into the host chromosome.

Guild succeeded in separating the two strands of DNA from each other. When each strand was tested separately in transformation, it was found that one strand is expressed phenotypically at once but that the other strand is not expressed until it has undergone one replication. This suggests that while both strands carry information for replication, only one strand can be expressed in the cell. This implication is in accord with other evidence indicating that only one of the two strands is transcribed during mRNA formation.

In Sueoka's laboratory, transformation has been used in a particularly ingenious experiment to arrive at a replication model for the bacterial chromosome. The investigators reasoned that the chromosome probably starts replication at a particular point (origin) and proceeds sequentially along the linear length, finally reaching the terminus. Thus, in an exponentially growing population, one would find twice as many chromosomes replicated near the origin end than near the terminal end (Figure 6·11), which would mean twice as much DNA representing genes at the origin end could be isolated from such a culture. This was tested by measuring the transformation frequency for markers located at different positions along the chromosome (Figure 6·11). A map was then constructed, based on marker-frequency analysis, that verified and extended the known linkage relationships. As a control, cells from the stationary growth phase showed equal marker frequency for all loci. Sueoka's model was later verified by direct isotope labeling of the marker DNA.

It is interesting that only rarely are two linked markers transformed

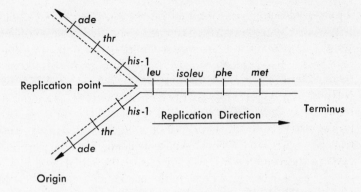

Origin

Transforming DNA isolated 2X *ade,* 2X *thr,* 2X *his-1,* 1X *leu,* 1X *isoleu,* 1X *phe,* 1X *met*

Figure 6·11. Analysis of replication model of the bacterial chromosome by transformation. DNA isolated from growing (replicating) cultures would contain two copies of those genes near the chromosome replicative origin.

simultaneously into the same host cell. Such is probably the case because the mechanisms of integration usually involve small sequences of nucleotides, probably with a molecular weight of less than 1 million. When genetic markers are sufficiently close, double transformation occurs. On the other hand, when the markers are on separate pieces of DNA, double events are rare.

In a few cases, transformation has been demonstrated between members of different but related species. Marmur has effectively applied this technique as a measure of evolutionary relationships similar to more conventional taxonomic techniques. It is not clear to what extent transformation may play a role in recombination in nature. However, as a laboratory tool, it has contributed in a major way to our understanding of the mechanism of recombination in bacterial systems.

The Mechanism of Genetic Recombination

Two major models have been proposed to explain genetic exchange or recombination. One hypothesis, that of *breakage-reunion,* dominated genetic thought for many years. More recently, as it became clear that recombination involved exchanges within DNA molecules, a new hypothesis, called *copy-choice,* was proposed. In the latter case, an exchange would occur only when a switch occurred from one template strand to another during replication.

The breakage hypothesis was developed in the early 1930s and was based primarily on cytological observations. During meiosis, chromosome pairing was observed, with the subsequent appearance of exchange figures (chiasmata). Presumably these figures were the result of reciprocal-exchange events resulting from simultaneous breakage and reunion of opposite ends of the chromatids. While it was clear that chromosomal duplication preceded the *appearance* of chiasmata, it was difficult to rule out the possibility that *effective* pairing occurred earlier, at which point the *real* exchange occurred. The best evidence concerning individual recombination events is derived from tetrad analysis, particularly in *Neurospora*.

TETRAD ANALYSIS

In certain fungi, algae, and bryophytes, it is possible to recover all the products of a single meiotic event. In the case of *Neurospora,* ascospores are laid down in an ordered pattern contained in an ascus sac. The ordering represents that pattern of assortment of chromosomes occurring at each meiotic division stage (Figure 6·12). Each spore contained in the ascus sac is haploid (one set of chromosomes)

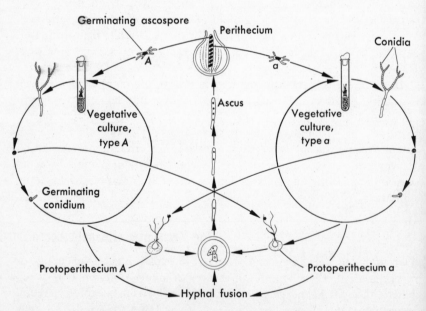

Figure 6·12. The life cycle of Neurospora crassa. Fertilization of one (haploid) mating type (A) by the opposite mating type (a). The zygote undergoes immediate reductive division, or meiosis, resulting in ascus sacs containing eight haploid spores. Each spore pair represents one of the four products of meiosis. Ascospores are isolated singly and in order from the ascus sac. [From Figure 15-7 of *Biology: Its Principles and Implications,* Second Edition, by Garrett Hardin. W. H. Freeman and Company. Copyright © 1952.]

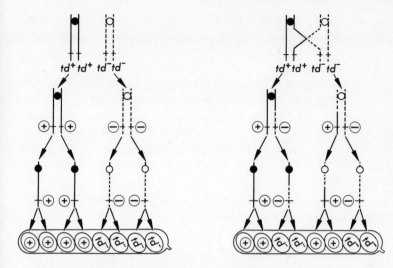

Figure 6·13. First and second division segregation in _Neurospora_.

and can therefore be analyzed directly without further crosses. Each ascus sac contains eight ascospores, sequential pairs of which are identical in genotype and represent one of the four products of meiosis. The position of a particular ascospore (pair) is determined by the orientation of separating chromosomes on a division spindle. For analysis, ascospores are removed singly and in order.

In a cross between a mutant (e.g., tryptophanless td^-) with a wild type (td^+), the ascus sac would contain four spores of each parental type. However, two patterns of ascospores in the ascus sac may occur. One is a 4:4 pattern, or td^+td^+ td^+td^+ td^-td^- td^-td^-, and the other a 2:2:2:2 pattern, or td^+td^+ td^-td^- td^+td^+ td^-td^-. The latter pattern represents what is to be expected if recombination between the gene and centromere occurs at a four-strand stage (Figure 6·13). Thus, the results of this study (and similar ones) constitute formal proof that four copies of the chromosome exist at the stage at which crossing over (recombination) occurs. If this were not true, tetrad patterns would always be 4:4 even when the marker gene is distal to the centromere.

Further evidence that a given crossover event involves only two of four strands comes from studies of patterns derived from double mutant crosses. When parents represented by AB and ab are crossed, both Ab and aB reciprocal-recombinant types are produced with equal frequency. In any given tetrad in which recombinant spores are found, one also finds the reciprocal-recombinant type as well as both parental types. Furthermore, either of the two strands of each parental chromosome can be involved in a crossover (at different sites), because two recombinant events can yield four recombinant but no parental progeny. That this is the case can be detected with three marker genes Such recombination is referred to as *four-strand doubles.*

Thus, both tetrad analysis and cytological observations are consistent with (1) crossover occurring at the four-strand stage; (2) occasional involvement of all four strands in crossover events, but only two strand at a given exchange; and (3) reciprocal exchange events (except in certain rare intragenic exchange phenomena). These rules, however apply only in recombination involving meiosis in cells with organized chromosomes.

BREAKAGE-REUNION VERSUS COPY-CHOICE

If in chromosomal systems all four strands are involved in recombination, the phenomenon could not be limited to the newly synthesized strands. Such a limitation is implied by a copy-choice hypothesis. As shown in Figure 6·14, copy-choice would usually involve reciprocal switching from one template strand to another.

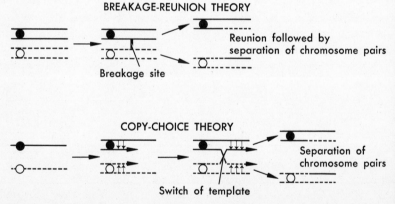

Figure 6·14. Breakage-reunion and copy-choice models of recombination Breakage-reunion involves actual exchange of chromosome arms. Copy-choice involves switching from one chromosome to another as a template during replication. The breakage-reunion hypothesis is now accepted.

Whereas breakage-reunion would require that recombinant chromosomes derive material (DNA) from *both* parental chromosomes copy-choice recombinant chromosomes would be all newly synthesized The two hypotheses were recently put to a test with isotopically heavy and light phage (λ) chromosomes. Heavy λ was crossed with light λ in *E. coli* cells growing in light media, and progeny DNA was isolated into heavy and light fractions by density-gradient centrifugation. Both progeny had appropriate genetic markers so that recombination could be detected in the labeled progeny. One would expect that if heavy label appeared in recombinant phage, this could only result from physical exchange between parental (light-heavy) chromosomes. On the other hand, if recombinants never contained heavy label, one would assume that the recombinants represented newly synthesized molecules only.

The results were striking in their support of the breakage-reunion hypothesis. Thus, in this case, modern molecular genetics did nothing more than verify what the early (1930s) cytogeneticists believed must occur. Many problems still remain unanswered. What is the mechanism of pairing between homologous chromosomes or DNA molecules? How is the breakage-exchange process mediated? What, indeed, is the detailed mechanism of recombination?

References

Adelberg, E. A., and J. Pittard. "Chromosome Transfer in Bacterial Conjugation," *Bact. Rev. 29:* 161, 1965.

Adelberg, E. A. (ed.) *Papers on Bacterial Genetics,* 2d ed., Boston: Little, Brown, 1966.

Braun, Werner. *Bacterial Genetics,* Philadelphia: Saunders, 1965.

Fincham, J. R. S., and P. R. Day. *Fungal Genetics,* 2d ed., Philadelphia: Davis, 1965.

Gunsalus, I. C., and R. Y. Stanier. *The Bacteria,* vol. 5, *Heredity,* New York: Academic, 1964.

Hayes, William. *The Genetics of Bacteria and Their Viruses,* New York: Wiley, 1964.

Hayes, W., and R. C. Clowes. (eds.) *Symp. Soc. Gen. Microbiol.,* vol. 10, *Microbial Genetics,* New York: Cambridge, 1960.

Jacob, F. and E. L. Wollman. *Sexuality and the Genetics of Bacteria,* New York: Academic, 1961.

Levine, R. P. *Genetics,* New York: Holt, 1962.

Rapier, J. R. *Genetics of Sexuality in Higher Fungi,* New York: Ronald, 1966.

Sager, R., and F. J. Ryan. *Cell Heredity,* New York: Wiley, 1962.

Whitehouse, H. L. K. *The Mechanism of Heredity,* New York: St. Martin's, 1965.

7

Gene Fine-Structure Analysis

GENETIC ANALYSIS—begun by Morgan in 1909 and continued in subsequent studies for many years—suggested that genes were discrete units and crossing over occurred *between* but not *within* them. Thus arose the concept of genes as beads on a thread (the chromosome) and the gene as a unit of recombination. Slowly we came to think of genes by other criteria as well. Mutant genes were identified and later induced by Muller so that the gene was considered to be a unit of recombination, but recognizable only because a mutation had changed its internal structure. The work of Beadle and Tatum in formulating their one-gene–one-enzyme hypothesis required that we further think of the gene as a unit of physiological function.

The *Drosophila* geneticist slowly accumulated a large number of mutants. Some of these appeared to be alleles, or mutations affecting a common functional gene. However, in the 1940s, E. B. Lewis and others showed that certain alleles (representing mutations of the same gene) showed recombination when crossed. These mutants were called pseudoalleles—a further indication of the reluctance of the geneticist to accept the possibility that recombination might occur *within* a gene.

It remained for Seymour Benzer to show, with bacteriophage, that recombination does indeed occur within the gene. It became clear that each gene contains a number of different sites that may mutate and that crossing over occurs between these sites. Study of the internal structure of the gene has come to be called *gene fine-structure analysis*.

The Classical Gene

Discussions in the previous chapter can be generalized to conclude that genes are arranged on chromosomes (be they bacterial, viral, or n higher plants or animals) in a linear fashion. The classical gene, as tudied primarily in diploid organisms, followed Mendel's laws of inieritance and acted as a particular unit. Different alternative states or illeles were required before a gene could be recognized and one allele (dominant) was usually expressed in preference over another (re-:essive).

By the early 1950s, it was clear that exceptions would have to be nade to the above concept of the gene because cases of what was :alled pseudoallelism became well known both in *Drosophila* and in naize. Pseudoalleles influence the same function but occasionally sepa-ate by recombination—which suggested they are not structurally illelic. Furthermore, pseudoalleles are expressed differently, depending >n whether they appear on the same chromosome or on different chro-nosomes. An example involves eye pigmentation in *Drosophila*. Wild-ype *Drosophila* have red eyes, and the white locus (w) prevents the ormation of pigment. Two alleles differ slightly, one (w) resulting in 10 pigment and another (w^{ap}) resulting in an apricot-colored eye. In he heterozygous state the eye is very pale. Progeny of heterozygotes ire rarely (1:1,000) recombinant types, namely w^+/w^+ (wild) and v/w^{ap} (double mutant). This suggests that w and w^{ap} are structurally lifferent but closely linked; the original heterozygote should be repre-

ented $\dfrac{w^+w^{ap}}{ww^+}$. From the double mutant a new type of heterozygote

nay be formed, namely $\dfrac{ww^{ap}}{w^+w^+}$. This fly has wild-type pigmented

yes. In other words, if the wild-type alleles are in the same chromo-iome (*cis* position), they are expressed as wild type; if they are in >pposite chromosomes (*trans* position), they are expressed as a mutant phenotype. Thus, these mutants are allelic in a functional sense but not in a structural sense and are called pseudoalleles.

Even these early studies suggested that the gene was internally com-plex and could mutate at different sites, with rare recombination events occurring between those sites—all internal within the func-tional gene. In subsequent discussions it should be kept in mind that the important aspect of the gene to the evolving organism is *function*. However complex or however simple, the gene remains as a biological unit that functions in the whole organism. We should not dismiss the term "gene" merely because a gene is complex or because we now understand it better in terms of structure and function.

Gene Fine Structure in Bacteriophage

Seymour Benzer, entering the field of genetics from a background in physics, was quite naturally attracted to the virus as an elemental system for analysis. He selected the rII region of bacteriophage T_4 mutants that could be recognized by characteristic plaques (clear areas where bacteria have been destroyed) when grown on certain strains of bacteria. For example, when a wild-type phage (r^+) grew on a lawn of *E. coli* B, small plaques with fuzzy edges resulted. Mutants at the *r* locus (rapid lysis) grew into larger plaques with sharp edges. Certain of these rapid-lysis mutants could be distinguished from all others when grown on other selective strains of *E. coli*. Mutants designated *r*II were unable to grow at all on *E. coli* strain K_{12}, later found to carry the prophage λ, thus creating K_{12} λ (Figure 7·1). This immediately provided a method of selection for the occurrence of rare recombinants between two r^- mutants, because only the r^+ recombinant type could grow on K_{12} λ. For such studies, Benzer isolated over three thousand independent *r*II mutants.

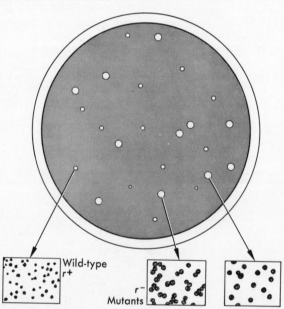

Figure 7·1. Diagram of mutant phage plaques. The spots (plaques) represent a clear area appearing within a lawn of bacteria. The small plaques are wild type (*r*+), and the larger plaques are rapid-lysis mutants (*r*). Benzer isolated large numbers of *r* mutants for his studies.

The selective technique employing host-range mutants was capable of detecting r^+ recombination frequencies as low as 0.00001 percent, or one recombinant per ten million progeny. For each r^+ progeny produced, a double mutant would be expected; thus the frequency of recombination is twice the frequency of r^+ phage in progeny from a quantitative cross. As might be expected, the various *r* mutants can be

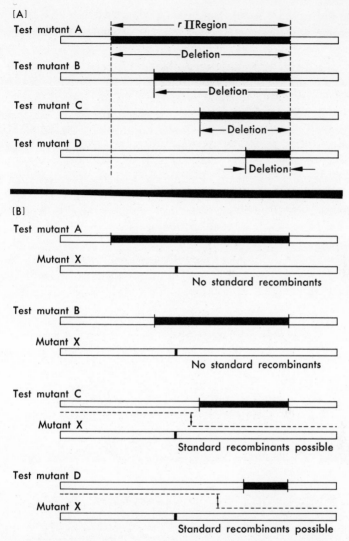

Figure 7·2. Deletion mapping. Certain rII (rapid-lysis) mutants of phage T_4 do not show recombination with large groups of point mutants that show recombination with each other. Any new mutant can be located within a segment by crossing it with tester (deletion) stocks. This facilitates rapid mapping of large numbers of mutants. [After Benzer. From "The Fine Structure of the Gene." Copyright © 1962 by Scientific American, Inc. All rights reserved.]

arranged into a linear map. Mutations sometimes occur that fail to show recombination in pairwise crosses. Certain of these proved to be particularly valuable.

If one has 3,000 mutants that must be mapped by all possible pairing combinations, one is faced with an impossible task even with phage (some five million crosses would be required). Benzer noted that certain mutants failed to show recombination with particular mutants that did recombine and that were grouped together in close linkage. He reasoned that these unusual mutants were really deletions for small segments of the rII region. His inference was supported by his observation that they failed to show reversion to wild type, a characteristic feature of most mutants. These deletion mutants were arranged into smaller and smaller inclusive classes on the basis of recombination experiments. Such deletion mutants were used as tester stocks to localize mutants within prescribed and limited genetic regions—thus eliminating many of the crosses required to map completely all 3,000 mutants (Figure 7·2). In addition, deletion maps were constructed from which Benzer formally proved that the gene was a linear, unbranched, noncircular structure. His proof of the linear topology of the gene was fundamental.

When all 3,000 mutants were fully analyzed, the rII region could be subdivided into about three hundred independent mutational sites—all of which could undergo recombination (Figure 7·3). The T_2 phage

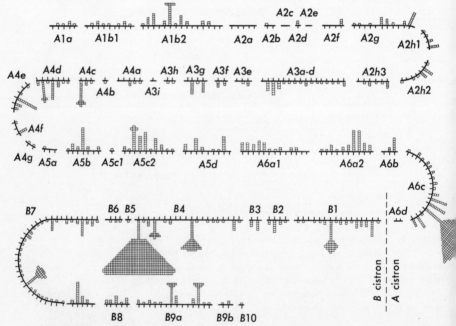

Figure 7·3. A map of the rII region of bacteriophage T_4. Segments are designated on the basis of deletion-mapping analysis. Each square represents one spontaneous mutant analyzed, thus each site is equivalent to a *muton;* and since they are positioned on the basis of recombination analysis, each site also represents a *recon*, the smallest element that can be exchanged. The rII region also contains two cistrons or functional units. [From Benzer, *Proc. Nat. Acad. Sci. 47:* 403, 1961.]

has some 200,000 nucleotide pairs and the *r*II region probably consists of less than 2,000 of them. This suggests that, on the average, no more than 7 base pairs separate these sites—indeed a fine dissection.

In general, a mutational site is equivalent to a recombinational site. However, there is some evidence that special techniques may be required to detect recombination within what appear to be identical sites. Benzer used two new terms to describe the two sites: the muton (the mutational site) and the recon (the recombinational site). The *muton* is the smallest element that, when changed, yields a mutation; the *recon* is the smallest element that can be exchanged (but not divided) by recombination. Our present concept, then, is that it is likely that the smallest unit of mutation is the nucleotide (pair) and that recombination may take place between adjoining nucleotide base pairs. (Formal proof of this will be discussed later, because Yanofsky has shown recombination *within* the coding triplet.)

We must again return to the unit of function to appreciate fully the fine structure of that highly complex unit, the gene (Figure 7·4). Early in his studies, Benzer simultaneously infected *E. coli* K_{12} λ with two *r*⁻ mutants. Certain mutant combinations result in wild-type phenotype (and lysis of K_{12} λ). On the basis of the simultaneous infection test, most *r*II mutants fall into two classes: A and B. These regions of complementation were called *cistrons* by Benzer. (This should be recognized as a special application of the *cis-trans* test dis-

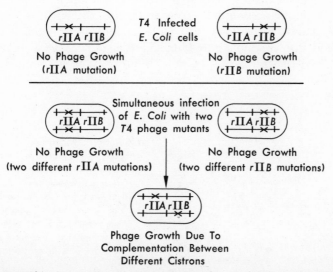

Figure 7·4. The cistron. The rII region consists of two subunits (cistrons) (rIIA and rIIB), which complement during simultaneous infection of *E. coli* K_{12} λ with mutants of T_4 phage.

cussed earlier in the analysis of pseudoalleles.) Benzer found himself in the same dilemma as had been faced by Lewis and others studying pseudoalleles in *Drosophila*. Were cistrons subunits of the same gene or did they represent adjoining genes, both of which were necessary for lysis of host cells and plaque formation? The question remains unanswered in the T_4 phage system, but the process has been described more effectively in *Neurospora* in which the gene product (enzyme) can be defined.

Genetic Complementation

The phenomenon of genetic complementation involves the interaction and recombination of gene products derived from homologous genomes present in the same cell. Such conditions are, of course, met in simple monohybrid crosses in plants and animals. From the point of view of examination and analysis of the gene product, however, these systems are not so valuable as is that of a simpler organism with a defined nutritional requirement. The filamentous fungus *Neurospora crassa* has been particularly valuable in complementation studies.

Neurospora forms heterocaryons as a result of hyphal fusion between strains with different genotypes, the nuclei remaining separate and replicating independently during vegetative culture. The cells along a mycelial filament are connected through continuous cytoplasmic bridges via pores in the connecting cell walls. Thus, nuclei and cytoplasmic components are free to pass from one cell to another and, indeed, from one portion of a mycelial mat to another. This results in a nearly homogeneous cytoplasm with random distribution of nuclei throughout the common cytoplasm. Thus it is possible with *Neurospora* to test the interaction of nuclear products in a common cytoplasm (Figure 7·5).

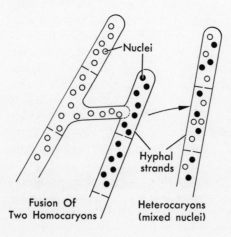

Figure 7·5. Formation of heterocaryons in *Neurospora*. When hyphal strands of the same mating type but different genotypes fuse, a heterocaryon is formed. Thus a heterocaryon is a mixed genotype in a common cytoplasm. Vegetative spores (conidia) formed from heterocaryons are also heterocaryons.

Nuclei

Hyphal strands

Fusion Of Two Homocaryons

Heterocaryons (mixed nuclei)

In bacteria it is also possible to form partial diploids (merozygotes), but this method has been applied mainly in studies of genetic regulation. As mentioned earlier, during transduction the donor DNA is frequently not integrated into the genome and partial diploids persist. Although this provides a sensitive quantitative test, it is limited in value for more precise studies of gene-product interaction. (The alkaline phosphatase system of Garen is a notable exception.)

The classical complementation analysis with bacteriophage was carried out by Benzer (as discussed earlier). Simultaneous infection of E. coli with two different bacteriophages resulted in a cooperative infection. From such an analysis of the rII genetic region, the concept of the cistron arose. Benzer's study was particularly timely in clarifying our concept of the gene.

Even as Benzer's definition of the cistron was becoming widely accepted, studies with Neurospora were forcing redefinition of the concept. Almost simultaneously, three groups of workers (Giles with the ad-4 locus, Fincham with the am locus, and Catcheside with the arginine system) brought an unusual situation to light. Each group had isolated large numbers of mutants that appeared to meet the criteria of the cistron for their respective locus. All mutants (for example ad-4) gave the same phenotype (a requirement for adenine and a deficiency of a particular enzyme), mapped together in a genetic cluster; also they all gave negative complementation tests in all combinations (no growth with combinations of mixed nuclei). However, a few pairing combinations appeared slowly as more mutants that showed complementation were isolated. This could be measured in several ways. One involved growth of the heterocaryon, whereas the component mutant systems grown independently showed no growth (Figure 7·6). More recently, the enzyme in question has been isolated, and it has been shown that all mutants are individually deficient in a particular enzyme activity. Such enzymatic activity is restored in complementing heterocaryons but not in combinations of mutants showing no complementation. In all cases examined there is evidence of multimeric enzymes or enzymes with a number of monomeric polypeptide-chain subunits. What is not always clear is whether all the monomeric units are identical or different in structure. If two mutants were defective in a particular enzymatic activity—one with a deficiency in one subunit and the other deficient in the second of two subunits—they might be complementary by each supplying the normal subunit to build the final enzyme (Figure 7·7). This is indeed the case in tryptophan synthetase, which will be discussed shortly.

There is evidence, however, that complementation does occur between mutants that are each defective in the same monomeric unit—although the final enzyme may consist of several of these identical

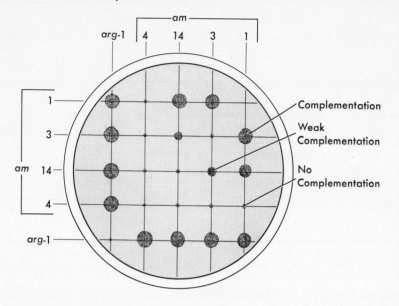

Figure 7·6. Complementation tests in Neurospora crassa. Five strains are tested in pairing combinations by mixing conidia at the designated location on the petri dish. Four mutations are allelic (different mutants of the *am* gene) and one is the nonallelic (different genes) mutation arg-1. Arg-1 complements fully with *am*; am^1 complements with am^3 and am^{14}; am^3 complements weakly with am^{14}; am^4 does not complement with any other *am* mutants. [After Fincham, 1966.]

subunits put together. It is extremely difficult to analyze subunit structure or the relationship between subunits, because enzymes can be isolated only after considerable effort and only in minute quantities.

The available evidence certainly leads to the conclusion that complementation does occasionally occur between the genetic structures specifying the sequence of a single polypeptide chain (Figure 7·8). These genetic subunits share with cistrons the property of noncomplementarity or complementation for the most part, but with exceptions in the case of particular mutant combinations. Furthermore, cases of differing degrees of complementation between pairs of mutants are very common and are usually related to the mutants' relative position in the chromosome. The reason is not clear for the surprising observation with two loci in *Neurospora* that there is an upper limit of 25 percent of normal enzyme activity in the best complementing combinations. Most pairing combinations produce low amounts of active enzyme, less formed as the mutons map closer to each other.

Several cases occur in which the enzymes produced as a result of

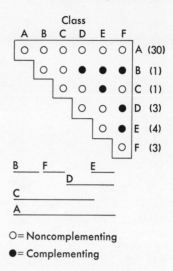

Figure 7·7. Principle of construction of a complementation map, as illustrated by mutants of the arg-1 series in Neurospora crassa. A: Patterns of complementation of six classes of mutants (number in each class is in parentheses). **B:** The representation of the results by a complementation map. The order of segments of B and F is arbitrary. [From D. G. Catchside, and A. Overton, in *Cold Spring Harbor Laboratory of Quantitative Biology,* 23: 137, 1958.]

complementation are qualitatively different from the wild-type enzyme. This observation probably provides the best support for the occurrence of complementation between mutants coding for structure within the *same* polypeptide chain. The hybrid-protein hypothesis was proposed to provide a mechanism for interallelic (intracistronic) complementation (Figure 7·9). The postulate made by several workers was that a normal enzyme is a homopolymer containing two or more identical chains, whereas the complementing enzyme was a heteropolymer consisting of chains derived from each mutant. The association of these altered chains, in combination, somehow resulted in cooperative compensation so that proper association and folding occurred and an active enzyme was formed. Such cooperative effects would not occur if all polypeptide chains were derived from either one of the mutant systems discussed above.

Figure 7·8. Hybrid protein hypothesis for complementation. The functional protein consists of two subunits that require the juxtaposition of site x and y, constituting an active (catalytic) center. A chain with mutant x (x^1) can complement a chain with mutant y (y^1) because the mixed dimer has one complete active center. [After Fincham, 1966.]

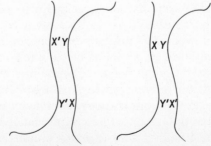

No Complementation   Complementation

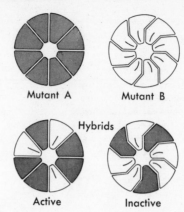

Mutant A   Mutant B

Hybrids

Active   Inactive

Figure 7·9. A model for complementation by conformational correction. The protein is supposed to be an octomer with subunits arranged, for simplicity of representation, in a two-dimensional radially symmetrical array. Mutant A produces a protein that is conformationally normal but has no complete active enzymatic center. Mutant B protein has a potentially active center (symbolized by a curved line in each subunit) but is inactive because of a conformational abnormality. Hybrids may, depending on the proportions of the two subunits, have either type of conformation. Subunits of mutant B protein, when present in conformationally normal hybrids, have a functional active center (symbolized by a straight line in each subunit). [From Fincham, *Genetic Complementation*, New York: W. A. Benjamin, 1966, p. 86.]

Recombination Within a Coding Unit (Triplet)

One of the most elegant studies in molecular genetics is that carried out by Charles Yanofsky on the tryptophan synthetase locus in *E. coli*. (This system was discussed earlier, at which time it was demonstrated that there was colinearity between the gene structure and the protein structure.) During his studies, Yanofsky discovered two cases in which different amino acids were substituted at the same position in the A protein of tryptophan synthetase. In two mutants (A_{23} and A_{46}) a single glycine residue was replaced by arginine and by glutamic acid, respectively. Two more mutants resulted in the similar substitutions of aspartic acid and cysteine for another glycine site.

Reversion studies with these four mutants were carried out and the amino acid substitutions analyzed. DNA codons (triplet bases) were assigned to all amino acids. Recombination studies were then carried out (by transduction), with these mutants differing in base changes within a single codon—a case of intracodon recombination.

Several crosses were carried out between these mutants. Recombinants (recognized as tryptophan-independent types) were obtained and analyzed for amino acid substitution at the original glycine site. For recombination to occur, it is necessary for the two recombining codons to differ by, not one, but two or three bases. If they differed at the same base position within the triplet, no recombination could take place between them. This is the case in two of the crosses—GAA (glu) crossed with GTA (val) and AGA (arg) crossed with ACA (thr); no tryptophan-independent recombinants were detected. In the four other cases in which tryptophan-independent recombinants were detected, the theoretical differences in the codons involved two or three base changes.

$$GAA \ (glu) \times AGA \ (arg)$$
$$GTA \ (val) \times AGA \ (arg)$$
$$GAA \ (glu) \times ACA \ (thr)$$
$$TGC \ (cys) \times GAC \ (asp)$$

In those cases where intracodon recombination occurs, the frequency is 0.001 to 0.003 percent, which is in full accord with the theoretical recombination frequency between nucleotide pairs (0.002 percent).

When the amino substitutions were examined in the recombinant

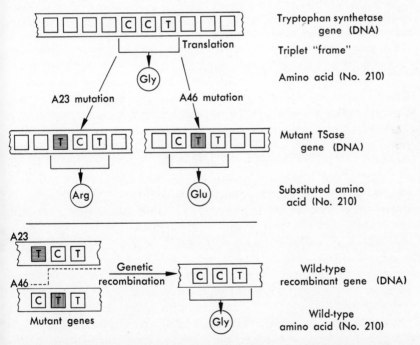

Figure 7·10. Recombination within a coding triplet. Two mutants (A_{23} and A_{46}) derived from wild type involve amino acid substitutions in the same position (210) in the TSase enzyme. When the mutants are crossed, a wild-type recombinant is recovered with the correct amino acid in position 210. This is consistent with a genetic crossover within the glycine-coding triplet from which a set of three normal bases segregate.

proteins, they were found to correspond to the expected substitutions as determined by known coding data (Figure 7·10). This is indeed recombination analysis at its highest degree of refinement.

Genetic "Punctuation": Gene-Gene Interface

All available information suggests that the genome, at least of bacteria and viruses, consists of continuous strands of DNA—in most cases a single molecule. If this is the case, one must consider the manner by which a cell can distinguish DNA belonging to one gene from that belonging to another. In other words, what connects one gene to the next—what are the "punctuation" symbols in DNA?

During the transcription process, mRNAs are formed that correspond to long stretches of DNA responsible for the formation of several enzymes (polycistronic mRNA). However, single enzymes are formed rather than a long protein in which linked enzymes are tied together tail to head. Thus, some process must terminate one peptide chain and initiate another. These punctuations might serve as satisfactory criteria in the determination of interfaces between cistrons.

Numerous mutants have been isolated in bacteria and phage that have altered triplets not corresponding to code words for amino acids. These have been termed *nonsense triplets*. Suppressor mutations for these triplets restore wild-type function. A hypothesis has been proposed that suggests that these triplets normally serve as recognition signals for chain termination in mRNA (Figure 7·11). When these particular triplets (UAG, UAA) are present in mRNA, they are recognized by two special tRNAs that carry no amino acid and thus

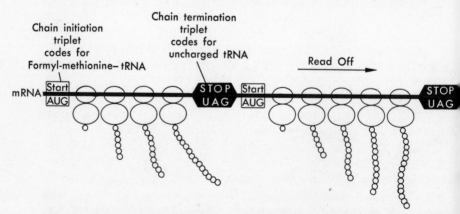

Figure 7·11. Models for genetic punctuation. Unique triplets in mRNA prevent the formation of a very long polypeptide chain with enzymes tied together tail to head. One—the stop triplet, UAG—codes for a blank (uncharged) tRNA; another—the start triplet, AUG (?)—codes for a tRNA charged with formylmethionine, thus blocking the formation of the peptide chain.

prevent further growth of the protein chain. The best feature of this model is the fact that chain termination (punctuation) represents only a modification of the accepted model of chain extension.

Again, in bacteria and phage, a mechanism for protein-chain initiation has been described. The studies were based on the observation that bacterial proteins frequently had methionine at the N-terminal (beginning) end rather than the expected random mixture. N-formylmethionine was then discovered, in which the amino group has attached a formyl group that prevents involvement in chain elongation. Normally, chain growth involves formation of a peptide bond between a carboxyl group (on an amino acid attached to the old chain) and an amino group (on the new amino acid). Such an attachment would be prevented by a formyl group attached to the amino group.

Thus, if there existed a codon for formylmethionine, this would provide a mechanism for both chain termination and chain initiation. The codon in mRNA for formylmethionine is probably AUG or UU. Its presence signals the attachment of N-formylmethionine, which must be the beginning amino acid. It has a free carboxyl that can attach to the next amino group in sequence until another punctuation codon is reached, at which point the functional peptide falls off the ribosome. It has been further suggested that, in vivo, the formylmethionine is removed by a trimming enzyme. The system is indeed a neat one. A unique sequence of bases says to protein synthesis "start here." The blocked amino group imposes a direction on protein synthesis; it prevents tail-to-head attachment of polycistronic messages by saying "stop" to any previous message.

In respect to punctuation codons, a more subtle function should be mentioned. All depends on unique types of tRNA molecules that have rare or perhaps no amino acids attached to them. A fine level of control of protein synthesis could be exercised through the regulation of the formation (or use) of these unique tRNAs. Indeed, Ames and Hartman have proposed such a model for the control of protein synthesis in an operon (the *modulation hypothesis* we discussed earlier). It is necessary to think in such terms when considering models for development in higher organisms.

Finally, returning to the main topic of this chapter, we probably will be best able to distinguish one gene from another by fully understanding the genetic language—not only the alphabet and the words but also the punctuation symbols in DNA.

References

Baker, W. K. *Genetic Analysis*, Boston: Houghton Mifflin, 1965.

Benzer, S. *Symp. Chemical Basis of Heredity, The Elementary Units of Heredity,* Baltimore: Johns Hopkins, 1957.

Fincham, J. R. S. *Genetic Complementation,* New York: W. A. Benjamin, Inc., 1966.

Hayes, William. *The Genetics of Bacteria and Their Viruses,* New York: Wiley, 1964.

Stent, G. S. *Molecular Biology of Bacterial Viruses,* San Francisco: Freeman, 1963.

Stent, G. S. (ed.) *Bacterial Viruses,* 2d ed., Boston: Little, Brown, 1965.

Whitehouse, H. L. K. *The Mechanism of Heredity,* New York: St. Martin's, 1965.

Prospective

GENETICS AS A FIELD has long since transcended any early and self-imposed limitation placed on it. As stated earlier, molecular genetics is concerned with the *storage, modification,* and *retrieval of macro-molecular information.* Such a definition, though arbitrary (and original, as far as I know), does provide adequate flexibility so that current studies at the interface with other fields may be included. The studies discussed here represent, in some cases, little more than preliminary observations or analytical measurements. I think they also represent three of the most exciting current research areas in molecular genetics. Perhaps they provide some prospective of the future.

The Genetics of Mitochondria

Until quite recently extrachromosomal heredity was considered to be nothing more than one of those esoteric phenomena that was fascinating but lay outside the mainstream of genetics. Recent studies, particularly with mitochondria and chloroplasts, have served to focus the attention of molecular biologists so that this subject is one of the two or three most active and exciting areas in genetic research today.

Mitochondria have been widely observed in respiring cells and have been shown to contain the major respiratory enzymes. When carefully isolated, most of the steps of electron transfer can be demonstrated in the mitochondrial particle. Structurally, the particle is complex, containing the two types of membranes that form a characteristic double membrane. The inner membrane is folded into what are called *cristae,* and it is on this surface that many of the enzymes of respiration and coupled phosphorylation are located.

Respiratory-deficient mutant strains of the fungus *Neurospora crassa* and of yeast have been isolated. *Neurospora* mutants are called *poky* because they grow slowly, and yeast mutants are called *petite* because the colonies are small. In both cases, when sexual crosses are carried out, the mutations cannot be located on any chromosome in the nucleus. Instead, the majority of such mutants exhibit what is called maternal or cytoplasmic inheritance. The respiratory-deficient character is transmitted, but only through the cytoplasm, to any progeny receiving the mutant cytoplasm. This observation (along with others) supports the view that poky and petite mutations are present in a genetic element exclusively in the cytoplasm.

The metabolic defect in these mutants is due to the simultaneous absence or alteration of several respiratory enzymes. In particular, cytochrome oxidase is deficient and the mutants are therefore insensitive to respiratory poisons such as carbon monoxide. In the case of *Neurospora*, the enzymatic activities differ depending on the age of a culture. A young culture is respiratory deficient and respiratory-poison resistant, but as it ages, the cytochrome spectrum becomes more nearly normal.

In *Neurospora* a number of respiratory-deficient mutants have been isolated that are very similar to poky, except that they are inherited as nuclear genes and the mutations can be mapped on particular chromosomes. It would appear that both the nucleus and a cytoplasmic factor can independently affect the activity of enzymes associated with mitochondria and, in turn, aerobic respiration. As we shall see shortly, this is probably because of the modification of the activity of enzymes when they are associated with altered mitochondrial membranes.

The major difficulty in these studies revolved around the question of purity of mitochondrial preparations and possible contamination by nuclear DNA. The observation that DNA isolated from mitochondria is qualitatively unique served as convincing evidence that contamination had been ruled out. In *Neurospora*, for example, the buoyant density of mitochondrial DNA was lower (1.701) than that of nuclear DNA (1.712). In other cases the two DNA species have not been distinguished, however.

In addition to the direct evidence noted above, it was observed that tritium-labeled DNA precursors (such as thymidine) are incorporated into both the nucleus and mitochondria. DNA synthesis in mitochondria is independent of DNA synthesis in the nucleus, however. When pulse-labeling studies were carried out, it became clear that the label in mitochondria was halved with each cell division and therefore stable. Furthermore, when density studies of the Meselson-Stahl type (see Chapter 1) were carried out, it could be shown that the DNA of mitochondria replicated in a semiconservative fashion.

These data, along with membrane-labeling studies with *Neurospora,* suggested that one mitochondria gives rise to two daughter mitochondria and mitochondria do not arise *de novo.*

A particularly interesting study involves the injection of poky mitochondria into the hyphae of a normal strain of *Neurospora.* The resultant hyphae grew more slowly and were recovered (exclusively) from an older injected culture. The mutant mitochondria not only express their own genotype and reproduce but do so to the exclusion of the normal host mitochondria.

A series of exciting observations has been made with the poky mutant in Woodward's laboratory at Stanford. Woodward and his coworkers have isolated the normal mitochondrial structural protein from wild type and a similar protein from a poky strain. When an amino acid analysis was carried out on the two proteins, it was found that they differed in only one amino acid—cysteine was substituted for a tryptophane in the mutant protein. This provides the first *direct* proof that a mutation in the mitochondrial genome results (as has been shown in the case of nuclear mutations) in a modification of the DNA in such a way that an incorrect amino acid is incorporated into a (structural) protein.

I have so far cited evidence for a mitochondrial genome, containing DNA replicated semiconservatively, that is expressed directly in a particular protein structure. In addition, two other exciting observations have been made concerning mitochondria. Protein synthesis has been shown to occur in isolated mitochondria; and tRNA molecules that are unique to mitochondria have been discovered.

Both RNA and protein synthesis occur in isolated mitochondria. RNA synthesis is inhibited by actinomycin D, which (as mentioned in Chapter 2) blocks DNA-directed RNA synthesis, thus suggesting a DNA-dependent RNA polymerase. All four ribonucleotide triphosphates are required for incorporation into RNA. Neither DNase nor RNase inhibit RNA synthesis in *intact* mitochondria. Hybridization studies between mitochondrial RNA and both nuclear and mitochondrial DNA suggest two types of RNA, one of which is complementary with nuclear and the other with mitochondrial DNA. This protein synthesis occurring in mitochondria may be under the control of mRNA from both the nucleus and the mitochondria itself.

Observations from Barnett's laboratory at Oak Ridge suggest an even more subtle control mechanism associated with mitochondria. It has been known for some time that two types of tRNA exist in the cell for each amino acid. One represented a major and the other a minor species. The Oak Ridge group have found the rare type of tRNA to be associated, in some cases, exclusively with mitochondria. Both the anticodon triplet of tRNA and specificity for the aminoacyl synthetase differ in some cases depending on the source of tRNA—the mitochondria or the cytoplasm.

In conclusion, the present view is that mitochondria exist in cells as true molecular symbionts, probably arising from an infective element not unlike a primitive bacteria. They have their own genome, their own DNA, and their own protein-synthetic apparatus. They appear to contain enzymes that are coded by nuclear genes and membranes coded by their own DNA. There is even some evidence that membranes of the cell other than those of mitochondria are under the control of the mitochondrial genome. A number of types (genomes) of mitochondria may simultaneously exist in a particular cell, thus providing a degree of subtle variation among cell types that has not previously been thought possible.

Many of the properties and characteristics described for mitochondria are also descriptive of centrioles and, in plant cells, of plastids. All these particles contain as much DNA as many viruses, which is sufficient to code for many different proteins.

The Molecular Basis of Memory and Behavior

It is clear that behavioral patterns are under the control of the genetic apparatus, because at least some of these patterns are as characteristic of a species as is its morphology or basic biochemistry. As in the case of development, the mechanism is far from clear, although information is likely to be stored in a macromolecule and released by some signal from the environment or from within the organism itself.

Although behavior is probably an extension of the developmental process, memory is temporal in nature and presumably not transmitted from generation to generation. It is not enough to say simply that memory is stored in the neuron, and two theories presently exist that differ in their explanations of the role of genes in the information storage and release process.

Experiments carried out some ten years ago in McConnel's laboratory with planaria have been cited widely but disputed by other investigators. The experiments suggested that planaria acquire conditioned responses by eating the RNA extracted from other planaria whose responses (e.g., to light) had been previously conditioned. It was postulated that memory consists of changes in the base sequence of RNA. Such changes might be due to the direct (or secondary) effects of electrical stimuli on neural RNA. In time, the memory-specific RNA might, in turn, exert some control over neural activity. Other experiments suggest that memory RNA is capable of replication because most RNA is degraded more rapidly than the rate of memory decay.

An alternative theory suggests that memory is more directly linked to the genetic apparatus. This model is really a modification of the operon theory (Chapter 5) and thus is a form of genetic regulation. Presumably, nerve cells undergo repression and derepression in response to electrical impulses, just as regulation occurs in response to such chemical stimuli as the metabolic inducers and repressors.

Neither model adequately explains how either macromolecule— RNA or protein—can affect the synaptic transmission of information between neurons, a presumed requisite for brain function.

It was Hydén who showed that the adenine-uracil ratio of RNA in the nuclei of rat neural tissue increased when the rats were exposed to a learning situation. Although it was originally proposed that the bases within RNA were modified, producing a new, qualitatively different RNA population, it is more likely that the relative amounts of transfer, ribosomal, and messenger RNA is changed through an inducton or derepression process.

Among his numerous proposals, Hydén suggested that changes in bases occurred by electrical signals causing frequency modulation. Under the influence of the modulated frequency, new bases could move into RNA and remain stable until protein synthesis occurs. This particular protein rapidly becomes dissociated somehow and combines with a complementary molecule; it is this complex that releases a transmitter substance that stimulates the next neuron. Presumably once the memory trace is established (the protein is synthesized), new identical impulses stimulate the protein directly and the impulse is transmitted along a circuit of cells. No other electrical pattern would so stimulate the protein to release the transmitter substance.

In summary, perhaps the most widely accepted view of the molecular basis of memory involves derepression of genes that, when free to function, produce proteins that provide for the passage of impulses through specific synapses. This would require no memory molecule but instead a pattern of facilitated synaptic connections.

Genetic Control of Development

Molecular genetics is poised on the brink of a frontal attack on what probably is now the central unsolved problem in biology. It remains to be seen whether the tools of molecular biology will prove to be as effective in studying the genetic control of development as they have been with other areas.

NUCLEI

Since the classic experiment by Spemann in 1914, a number of workers have carried out experiments that involve the removal or transplanting of nuclei from various developmental stages to other, usually earlier stages. In some limited cases, old nuclei are still capable of directing the development of enucleated eggs. In certain unsuccessful cases, eggs do not develop because of obvious chromosomal abnormalities. However, in most cases, such as with the experiments of Briggs and King, a host egg cannot proceed beyond that stage attained by the nuclei used for transplantation. This suggests that nuclei undergo differentiation and that this process is irreversible.

There seems to be little doubt that RNA transfer occurs from the nucleus to the cytoplasm. In some cases this RNA can be protected and drawn from storage during the early stages of differentiation.

CHROMOSOMES

One of the most active and promising areas for the study of the genetic control of development involves the chromosome itself. It is clear that all chromosomes in a particular cell do not replicate at identical times. Taylor has recently demonstrated that, in addition, chromosomes do not replicate simply from one end to the other but instead consist of as many as several hundred replicons that undergo replication simultaneously. Each is approximately as large as a phage genome, and presumably each has its own unique replication-initiation site. It is interesting to speculate whether factors that regulate replication of the bacterial replicon also play a role in the replication of organized chromosomes of higher organisms.

Chromosomes of the salivary glands of *Drosophila, Rhynchosciara,* and *Chironomus* (all insects) have proved to be valuable experimental material for studies of chromosome differentiation. These and other tissues contain the giant polytene chromosomes, which arise by repeated duplication of DNA without separation. Puffs and constrictions occur along the length of such chromosomes that are characteristic for a particular tissue at a given time in its development. The same tissue at other times may have a very different pattern of puffing. Different tissues show different patterns in respect to particular puffs and no differences in other regions. Beerman believes puffs occur during periods of gene activity. He has observed unique sequences of puffing during development of a particular tissue.

Major changes in patterns occur near the end of the larval stage and during the early stages of pupation. Pupation is stimulated by a hormone called ecdysome; injections of larvae with this hormone result in a marked and immediate change in certain puffs.

In tissues such as the amphibian oöcyte almost the entire chromosome appears to be active. Presumably certain genes that are never needed again in the adult organism function during early development. Near the end of oögenesis the synthetic machinery for both RNA and protein is very low. Thus a mechanism must exist for activation of genes and their later repression. In addition, the RNA produced during the active stage is conserved until fertilization occurs.

In summary, there is much evidence that cellular differentiation is associated with the differential activation of the subunits of the chromosomes.

GENES

ISOZYMES.   A number of enzymes exist in molecular forms called isozymes. All isozymes function in a similar role in catalysis but may differ in substrate specificity and in physical properties. In the case of lactic dehydrogenose (LDH), studied by Markert, five forms are known to exist. The chick heart contains, throughout development, one type (LDH$_1$). In skeletal muscle, a gradual shift occurs from the heart (LDH$_1$) to the muscle (LDH$_5$) form of enzyme.

LDH can be split into four polypeptide chains that are of equal size but distinguished by electrophoresis. LDH$_1$ is composed of four identical subunits (B) ; LDH$_5$ contains four other but also identical subunits (A). The other three isozymes (LDH$_2$, LDH$_3$, LDH$_4$) are mixtures of types A and B subunits. Since separate genes control the synthesis of the A and B polypeptides, the expression of these genes must somehow be regulated during development.

HEMOGLOBIN.   There are at least five different genes in the frog that are concerned with the synthesis of hemoglobin. Certain of these genes are activated during early development, others at metamorphosis. The switch from tadpole to adult hemoglobin may be abrupt; if it is, it would provide a model system for the temporal activation of genes. However, it is not known whether a particular cell is capable of producing both types of hemoglobin or whether adult hemoglobin is produced by cells that previously did not actively produce any hemoglobin. The evidence is that the switch from tadpole to adult hemoglobin may be stimulated by hormones. Although this would provide a mode, it does not provide a mechanism.

In man, the different hemoglobins reflect single gene mutations with the subsequent substitution of a single amino acid (see Chapter 4). In addition, the hemoglobins of the embryo and adult differ. Fetal hemoglobin gradually disappears by the fourth month after birth, but certain mutations occur in man that result in the continued production of fetal hemoglobin even in the adult. Thus again, a mechanism must exist for the temporal production of a particular protein molecule during development.

ENZYME REGULATION.   Although the operon theory provides an appealing model for the regulation of enzymatic activity, no really clear-cut examples of substrate induction exist in higher organisms. Most enzymes are constitutive in such systems, and although various factors stabilize particular enzymes, true induction of the bacterial type may be a rare phenomenon. That end-product repression has been demonstrated in the chick provides a mean for regulation of enzymatic activity but not for synthesis.

Agents such as hormones stimulate enzyme production and may play a major role in the regulation of gene activity in both plants and animals. Indeed, this would appear to be the mechanism of action of hormones.

RNA Patterns. The unfertilized egg contains a wide assortment of RNA, including ribosomal and transfer. Some messenger RNA is also present, because somehow fertilization stimulates the translation process, and protein synthesis and considerable differentiation can proceed after fertilization without new RNA synthesis. One of the major unsolved problems is the means by which the unfertilized egg restricts RNA translation into protein until fertilization occurs. Perhaps the initial attachment between the ribosome and mRNA that forms polysomes cannot occur. In any case, polysomes appear to be rare in eggs. Another alternative is that protein synthesis may be restricted by the presence of certain rare tRNA species that regulate the initiation of translation.

Not only is protein synthesis limited in eggs, but no RNA synthesis occurs after the eggs mature. Thus transcription is also repressed and, in turn, released upon fertilization. This stage of regulation would seem to occur directly at the level of the gene. As differentiation proceeds, a new pattern of RNA synthesis would occur.

It is of interest to note that polysomes exist that cannot proceed with protein synthesis until a particular developmental stage is reached. This could be because of the presence of a rare sequence of triplets that cannot be translated until tRNA carrying the proper anticodon is produced or released.

Certain messenger-RNA molecules seem to be very stable and undergo repeated rounds of protein synthesis. Just why some messengers are stable and others unstable is far from clear.

Morphogenesis in Phage. One of the more interesting models for gene control of morphogenesis is the conditioned lethal-mutant system of T_4 bacteriophage. Following infection of a sensitive bacterium with a phage, certain events occur. A series of enzymes concerned with the synthesis of phage DNA is formed immediately following infection. Subsequent to this process, the protein components of the phage are synthesized and assembled into a complete phage. Phage mutants have been isolated that are deficient in a particular developmental feature and thus stop the process at some intermediate stage.

These mutants were isolated in two ways. Some are lethal at higher temperatures (42°C) but form plaques at lower temperatures (25°C). Others, called conditional lethal mutants, form plaques upon infection of particular bacterial strains but not of other strains. When these mutants are mapped around the circular chromosome of phage, their location is strikingly nonrandom. Groupings of genes occur involving either defects in DNA synthesis or defects in maturation. Within these genetic regions, more specific subregions occur. For example, the maturation region contains mutants that produce head membranes only, both head membranes and free tail fibers, particles with contracted sheaths, tails only, or none of these components. Some appear normal but are inactive.

Thus it appears that in phage, genes are grouped on the chromosome into an early-function (DNA-synthesis) region and a late-function (maturation-of-phage) region. It remains to be seen, however, whether such organization in the chromosome is similarly represented as a temporal transcription or translation process. Indeed, evidence exists suggesting certain late gene products are produced early but are not expressed until a later stage.

Early- and late-function regions have been demonstrated in λ phage also. Szbalski has shown in a recent study that both strands (W and C) are transcribed but not in an overlapping fashion. For example, following injection, one particular region starts to be transcribed. This early transcription continues to be read off the W strand and is required for the initiation of transcription of the late region, which itself occurs from the C strand of DNA. Indeed both transcription (RNA synthesis) and translation (protein synthesis) are required for the initiation of transcription of the late-gene region. A mechanism clearly exists for the temporal control of gene transcription. Proteins are required in this case to extend the transcription process to other genes.

References

Bell, E. (ed.) *Molecular and Cellular Aspects of Development,* New York: Harper & Row, 1965.

Bonner, J. *The Molecular Biology of Development,* Fair Lawn, N.J.: Oxford, 1965.

Gaito, J. (ed.) *Macromolecules and Behavior,* New York: Appleton-Century-Crofts, 1966.

Granick, S., and A. Gibar. "The DNA of Chloroplasts, Mitochondria and Centrioles," *Prog. Nucleic Acid Res. and Mol. Biol. 6:* 143, 1967.

Jinks, J. L., *Extrachromosomal Inheritance,* Englewood Cliffs, N.J.: Prentice-Hall, 1964.

Sager, Ruth. "Mendelian and Non-Mendelian Heredity: A Reappraisal," *Proc. Roy. Soc. (Ser. B), 164:* 290, 1966.

Wagner, R. P., and H. K. Mitchell. *Genetics and Metabolism,* New York: Wiley, 1964.

Wilkie, D. *The Cytoplasm in Heredity,* London: Methuen, 1964.

Index

131